How to Use
PORTABLE
POWER TOOLS

The portable saw is the means to greater volume in modern building.

How to Use
PORTABLE
POWER TOOLS

By MAURICE H. REID

Author of "How to Use Hand Tools"

THOMAS Y. CROWELL COMPANY : New York

749.13
R

Acknowledgment is made to the Porter-
Cable Machine Company for all photographs not otherwise credited.

PREFACE

The days of laborious drudgery and painstaking, slow hand labor of the builder's and carpenter's trade are now long past. The quiet but effective revolution that has taken place in the building and handicraft trades has boomed the building business to a level many times greater than the peaks of the pre-war years. Private construction this year will run well over a million new homes. In 1920, the production was only 247,-000. By percentage to population, we have fewer carpenters working shorter hours today than their fathers did back in the boom of the '20's. What is even more phenomenal, these carpenters of today are turning out better work as well as five times the volume.

How is it possible? Mass development methods, smaller and better-designed houses, materials that are easier to use, prefabrication, and other factors are a part of the answer. The big contribution, however, to today's high-speed and large-volume building was made by the development of portable power tools. This new industry got its start around the early '20's when fractional-horsepower electric motors became available. Since then, an electric high-speed tool has been devised for almost every manual chore imaginable. The magic of electric power has greatly speeded up and improved the work of the plumber, electrician, repairman, garage mechanic, heating man, mason, and factory assembly worker, as well as the carpenter and shop craftsman. All of these workers can now take the power of the shop and the accuracy of precision equipment directly to the job site, wherever it may be.

With modern metals and advanced designs, these tools have also greatly extended the variety of work that the manual worker is able to do. The woodworker of former years can now apply his skill with the same efficiency to plastics, stone, marble, fiber materials, metals, glass, and a host of new products of this chemical age. The home craftsman and the beginner in the trades can now learn to operate these new portable power tools and can turn out first-class work in much less time than his predecessor with his long apprenticeship.

The greatest boost given to the manufacturers of power tools has been by the home craftsman and the new generation of homeowners who have so much to do around the house and so little money and time with which to do it. Portable power provided the answer. Today, it is estimated that there are around 11 million home shops in this country. In 1952, these converts to the "do-it-yourself" school built, entirely or in part, over 250,000 of their own homes. The home craftsman, with portable power tools, built more houses than the professional builder did back in 1920! He has become a pretty capable fellow, indeed!

It is the purpose of this book to explain the operation of the popular portable power tools of today and to show how they can be further applied to advance the product of the professional, as well as the home, craftsman. Perhaps some of the ideas explored here will help this great army of producers. It is to them that this book is dedicated.

CONTENTS

How to Use
PORTABLE
POWER TOOLS

1 ≡ PORTABLE POWER—
THE MODERN TOOL

Portable power requires new technique. The introduction of portable power tools to the manual trades brought a great many changes in the manner of working and introduced many problems that were not present when working with ordinary hand tools. The direction of making a saw cut, for instance, was reversed. The hand saw made its cut from the far side of the wood to the worker's side. The table saw also cuts in the same direction, and from the top of the board down. But the portable hand saw cuts from the bottom of the board up and from the workman's side out to the far side. This and other differences found in the operation of these new tools demand a different approach in laying out work, marking, clamping, and setting up for working, and in making the actual operations.

Safety is another important factor, both for the worker and for the material he is working on, that has changed materially with the advent of portable power tools. In the design of the tools, the manufacturer has, in every case, included safety guards over blades, ground wires for electric shock hazards, an automatic slip-clutch to prevent kickback, finger tip controls, and other types of devices that reduce the hazards

1

of using electric power. The one outstanding feature of portable tools that makes them so valuable in use is also one that makes them more dangerous to use. The power saw cuts many times faster than the hand saw. The electric drill turns about 1000 times a minute as compared with the hand drill speed of around 120 turns a minute. The router blade runs at a speed of 22,000 revolutions per minute. Speed is the one big feature that makes these tools so valuable. Not only do they cut faster with that speed, but they make a smoother and more accurate cut. Also, because of this speed factor, both the tools and the materials on which they are used must be handled more carefully than was necessary with hand tools. Mistakes can be made just as rapidly as an accurate cut.

Former methods of making cabinet joints, drilling holes for fasteners, fitting parts together, and finishing work for painting have changed greatly. For instance, most cabinet joints formerly required a careful layout and marking for cutting with the hand saw, the drill, and chisel. It was a tedious job to make a dovetail joint with hand tools. Today the same joint can be quickly clamped in a dovetail fixture and both sides routed out at the same time. The pieces fit perfectly! No marking, sawing, or chisel work is necessary. With the use of the small electric hand drill, holes can be made where needed as the work progresses. Formerly, it was necessary to plan all such holes in advance and make them on the shop drill press before the assembly began. In the assembly, many pieces can be cut and fitted right to the job as they are needed. It is no longer necessary to go back to the shop or to measure and make every piece in advance. With the fast-moving finishing sanders, the work can be cleaned up for painting within a few minutes after the job is finished. No longer is it necessary to give each piece a thorough shop sanding and do the laborious finish work by hand.

Fig. 1. The portable drill can work in any direction or position.

Fig. 2. The table saw cuts from back to front and from the top of the board down.

Types of tools are many. The newcomer to the field of portable power will probably be overwhelmed by the abundance of types, makes, sizes, speeds, shapes, and accessories of power tools found in the stores. The number of these tools is increasing almost every day. Like most everything else, however, there are good ones and there are those not so good. Every time a really good tool is introduced on the market, there quickly follows a host of imitators and "similar" gadgets. The buyer must learn to recognize the essential features of a good tool and be able to select from among the many possibilities those tools that can give him the quality performance he is after.

Basically, there are only six or seven types of power tools made, depending on how you wish to classify them. A few general types of accessories for each tool are very practical.

The beginner who understands the fundamental use of each basic tool and the possible adaptations can quickly distinguish the better and more durable tools from the cheaper varieties.

There are three types of portable saws on the market, all of which have an important use for particular applications. The foremost of these is the circular saw commonly available in blade diameters of 6 and 8 inches for ordinary use and home shop construction and the 10- and 12-inch blades for heavy construction and industrial use. All of them operate on the same principle and with various controls and settings. The vibrating, or reciprocating, saw uses a straight blade very much like that of the hacksaw or scroll saw. These are excellent tools for very small work such as models and hobby crafts, but they have little use in the professional trades or the average home shop. Some of these saws hold a short blade only at one end and others are built with a frame very similar to that of the scroll saw. The latter operates by vibrating a very thin blade for fine and delicate work. The chain saw is the third basic type of portable saw and is built for rough cutting of trees, logs, and timbers. Its blade is a chain of teeth that moves around a fixed support which projects from the motor body.

The drills are merely drills. This is not to belittle the very valuable family of drilling tools but simply intends to say that, although there are many sizes of drills, they all operate on the same principle. A motor is held in a convenient type of housing to which a handle and perhaps an extra guiding device is attached. The shaft holds a device called a chuck which is situated at the working end of the tool. This chuck, in turn, holds the drills and other accessories which the tool is designed to operate. As for accessories, the drill can be made to drive almost anything with the proper attachments—and the attachment is usually available. Unfortunately, in both quality of

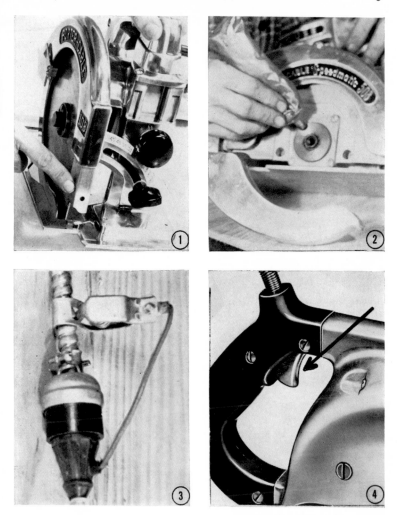

Fig. 3. Safety is an important part of tools. (1) The front safety guard shields saw blade at all cutting depths. (2) The safety clutch and the blade guard (blade removed). (3) Ground connection provided for electric cords of all tools. (4) Finger-tip switch provides instant control of machine.

the tool itself and the attachments it is made to drive, many of the offerings on the market are little short of ridiculous. This field of electric drills has been the most abused of all in the power-tools market.

Sanders are of three types: the belt, vibrating or reciprocating, and the rotary disk. The last-named is most commonly used as an accessory for the electric drill; although, for heavy sanding, the load is often too much for the common type of light hand drills. The more recently developed routers, shapers, and planers are really a development of the electric drill, using a more powerful motor and a frame device for guiding the tool.

Hedge shears, wool clippers, and other such tools operate by the use of a cam and eccentric or a vibrating movement. The hedge clipper (figure 38) uses a continuous link chain which moves around a cutting bar. Other tools, such as the flexible shaft, electric wrench, and the screwdriver, are extensions of the direct rotary action of the drill.

Electric paint sprayers, air hammers, jacks, body tools, chipping tools, nailing devices, and some sanders are not electric tools in the true sense of the word. They get their power directly from a compressed air hose which is connected to a tank. An electric motor is usually the source of compressor power, but the tool itself operates by the force of the air going through its mechanism. We will not include this group of tools in this book.

How to buy the best tool for your money. Unfortunately, price is a poor indication of value, as you will find out when you shop for power tools. This is a serious matter to all workmen because it is necessary to have good tools in order to turn out good work. Portable power tools cost more than ordinary hand tools and a mistake in their purchase is more to be regretted than a simple error in buying the wrong chisel or screwdriver. Durability and reliability of the tool are of utmost importance. The design and construction of the tool are important to the type of use to which it is intended. Light shop work demands a tool that is light and easy to handle, well balanced, and accurate for working on small stock. The demands of farm work, building, and heavier trades require a tool of stronger frame, yet one not tiring to use. It must be accurate and with control settings that are easy to use, yet stay in place. The frame must be such that is not easily damaged around busy work areas.

When inspecting the tool before you buy, look at the adjusting devices to see if they are well marked and do actually measure the degree of the setting. Inspect the threads of bolts and set screws to determine whether they can be easily damaged. Soft materials in such places can be easily stripped of threads, bent, or otherwise rendered useless by even a slight accident. Is the metal of the base substantial or can it easily be bent out of shape or alignment? Do the clamping or holding devices of the tool fasten securely or will they be easily pulled out of position? This is very important on sanders.

Further inspection should consider the matter of personal safety. Do the guards close completely around the blade and work freely on the saws? Is the switch located so that it can be easily used yet not accidentally turned on or off? Balance the tool in the hand, run the motor, notice the vibration, if any, the noise, the start and stop. Finally, there is that all-important factor called "feel" of the tool. This one cannot be defined. You have to use the tool and like it. The companion to this last-named quality of good tools is that thing called "pride of ownership." The salesman knows what it is, but he can't tell you. You just have to feel good about using and owning the tool to be really satisfied.

All of the tools explained and illustrated in this book were selected because they come nearest to satisfying all the desirable qualities of good portable power tools. Furthermore, all the directions and adjustments apply to all good tools. Whatever make of tool you happen to own or buy, you will find, if it is made to meet standards of precision and quality that are demanded by all trades, that the comments and suggestions in this book will apply to your tools as well as the ones shown here. As you look at the pictures and diagrams, you will learn to recognize the necessary and desirable qualities of really good tools so that, whatever you buy, you will have a standard of value with which to judge.

There is one observation that should be made regarding the general quality of portable power tools on the market. Some manufacturers have been in the business of making fine machines for the professional trades for forty years or more. Others have come into the market with lighter-built and cheaper tools to capture the ever growing trade of the craftsmen and homeowners. As this business grew and competition increased, the older firms met the demand for a time by adding a line of good tools that were built on a lighter frame, with a smaller motor, and priced to meet the popular market. These tools were generally marketed under a distinct trade name. After a few years, some of the more astute manufacturers made careful customer classification of their sales and found that many of the homeowners and week-end craftsmen were buying the heavier professional tools and builders and carpenters were buying the lighter models! As a result, these special brands are now being dropped and the manufacturers are beginning to make just one line with several models to meet various needs.

Select the right tool for the job. No greater words of sound advice were ever given to the man setting out to buy portable power tools. Good tools are worth every penny of their cost, but they still cost money. Buying the wrong tool or the wrong size of tool is a waste of considerable value. The first decision that must be made in order to select the right tool is to evaluate the job. When a man is to be hired for a given task, the first thing the employer does is to set down the requirements of the job, or write up the job specifications for the personnel department. A man must be hired who can fill those specifications. You have to do the same thing in buying tools.

What type of work are you going to do? How often will you be running the machine? How frequently will you be using it? Will you be cutting light materials or heavy, house-construction wood? Will the motor be running steadily or intermittently? Is wood the only material involved or will you be working on metals, stone, plastic, or composition materials? Is the work simple in operation or will you need a variety of accessories and adapters for special tasks? These questions must all be answered; and, as you go through this book, many others will come to mind as you consider the tools you need.

There is one aspect of buying tools, and particularly portable power tools, that cannot be overstressed. It is the reliability of the manufacturer of the tool and his service arrangement through the local dealer. As for the maker of the tool and his reputation, you can easily check a few stores that sell to professional workers. Ask around in the trade and find out what the everyday working man thinks of different brands of tools. Then check with your dealer and learn whether he carries a good stock of accessories, extra blades, spare parts, and other tools by the same manufacturer. Nothing is more disconcerting than to find out that you have to ship the tool eight hundred to a thousand miles to have it repaired. Good distribution today demands authorized service centers in every large city. Good dealerships also demand a good supply of tools, parts, and accessories.

Make sure that you can get good service before spending your money for a particular tool. The best way to do this is to look at and read the manufacturer's literature which comes with the tool. Make sure that it includes a repair and spare parts list for that particular model. Also make sure that it includes a list of the authorized repair stations with complete addresses. Go ahead and buy as good a tool as you can afford, but be sure that it will meet your requirements. It need not be more tool than you require, but more mistakes are made in buying insufficient power and quality than otherwise. Remember that a small or poorly powered tool cannot do a heavy duty job. The better tool can always do the lighter job with no trouble.

Measuring the work load. In judging the type of tool you need for a particular job, think of the work load that you will demand of the machine. It would be rather silly to try using a 10-inch saw if you are working on ship models or fishing lures. When you are framing a house or building furniture, however, you will need a fairly hefty saw. The hobbyist, jeweler, model maker, and all workers on small objects will need light tools that have wide versatility and that can operate for long periods without overheating. Builders and repairmen working on houses need tools that will stand up under heavy loads and that can do many tasks without elaborate changes of fittings and accessories. In between these extremes there are the medium-light tools for the occasional worker. There are also special blades and accessories for the millwright, cabinetmaker, plumber, electrician, farmer, engine and general mechanic. Above all, if your time is valuable, the accessories must be such that they can be attached and changed easily on the tool.

Weight and balance of the power tool is particularly important if you use your tools on a scaffold, up on the roof, in the attic, or other places where a very heavy tool will be tiresome and awkward to use. Balance and comfort to the hand is an individual matter. The power of the tool is largely a matter of working speed. No tool should be forced into the work beyond its capacity to cut easily. This applies to all power tools. Overloading the drive will wear out the tool faster than any amount of normal usage. Blades must *always be kept sharp* to get the best service from your tools. As a final word, be sure you buy a tool that is equal to the job, make sure that it is easy to use and one which you will be proud to own.

As for the quality of the motor and its ability to stand up under usage, you have to go very largely by the manufacturer's specifications and guarantee. As you read the descriptions of various tools in this book and measure their uses against your needs, you'll get a pretty good idea of the work-load capacity and motor specifications that you need. When you talk to your dealer, make sure that he knows what you expect the tool to do. See that the manufacturer's description of a particular tool includes the type of work you have in mind. If you and the dealer fully understand each other on this point, and the machine carries a good manufacturer's guarantee, you are not likely to go wrong.

Portable power tools are essential. We have already mentioned the degree to which portable power has revolutionized the work of modern craftsmen. It is true that, in order to handle modern materials adequately and to put out the volume of work demanded by competition today, the workman in every field of manual arts cannot work without some types of portable power equipment. This is so for several reasons. These devices were invented to meet a real need. They have been improved enormously in a short time because of their widespread use and popularity. Portable power tools have won a permanent and highly useful place both in the shop and on the job site.

In the shop, for instance, the handling of large sheets of plywood has always been a problem. With fixed, stationary machines, the sheet of wood measuring 4 feet by 8 feet or larger is difficult to handle without table extensions and elaborate supports. Even these setups often require two men for accurate cutting. With the portable saw, the sheet of plywood can be left on the pile, raised from the next sheet by strips of scrap wood, and cut as desired by one man. It is much easier to move the portable saw across the board than it is to move the board through the stationary saw. Furthermore, many operations and alterations can be made in the work as the assembly progresses. Formerly it was necessary to complete all parts first and do all the fitting and joining by hand. There are also many occasions in the shop when table machinery is set up for a production job and cannot be used for small, short-run work without costly knockdown and resetting. The portable saws, drills, sanders, planers, and shapers can be used at any time and at any location merely by plugging the connection into the wall outlet, picking up the tool, and pressing the trigger.

In the school shop and in vocational training classes, portable tools have enabled group work to proceed at a much faster pace. Many schools now have several of each type of power tool where formerly they could afford only one or two stationary power tools. More students can work faster with portable power in a given class period. Shop maintenance and production work in factories, particularly on assembly lines, has been vastly improved and speeded up by the use of portable power.

As for the plumber, carpenter, electrician, heating and ventilating man, and others in the building trades, no modern workman would last very long in these trades without the speed and convenience of portable power tools. The carpenter can use two sizes of saws, the 6 inch for trim, siding, wallboard, flooring, etc., and the 10 inch for studding, floor joists, stair treads, and all heavier work. He also needs two sizes of electric drills, the ¼ inch and the ½ inch. A light finish sander will be sufficient for all sanding operations unless he is finishing floors. If he has to do much rough finishing and built-in work, a heavy-duty belt sander is an essential.

The plumber, electrician, and heating man use the 6- or the 8-inch saw, a light belt sander, and the ½-inch drill. The drill is necessary for running wiring, conduit, pipes, and for locating and starting openings for fixtures and ducts. Even the roofing and siding experts, tree surgeons, and painters find the small saws, belt sanders, and drills useful in their daily tasks.

Around the farm and for home maintenance three basic tools are needed for the jobs usually encountered. The electric saw should be a really good, heavy-duty 8-inch or 10-inch machine. A light, ¼-inch capacity drill is necessary for light drilling and grinding. Where any heavy work is encountered, a larger ½-inch drill should be included. A good belt sander of fairly heavy frame and with a 2-inch or 3-inch belt completes the basic requirements.

The average user of portable tools is not the man who works in his home shop as a hobby, but the man who not only finds such work enjoyable but has to do it of necessity. Homeowners who want to make alterations or additions to the house, remodel or build a new home, make their own furniture or garage, build a boat, finish off the attic of the new home, or even make an extra buck in the shop on evenings and week ends are the average users. Where did these people come from? A great many of them are nonmanual working men—clerks, lawyers, bank presidents, real estate dealers, and salesmen (and saleswomen)—who learned to work with tools in defense plants during the last war. Many of them started as the result of bitter experience in trying to hire such jobs done by professional workers. The cost of hired labor has gone up and the quality of work that the amateur can do with modern power tools has made him a successful competitor. Other factors are the general inflation of prices and the great American desire to "get things done," along with a general longing for a really creative outlet. People love to work with their hands and they have more time in which to do it.

This average user we speak of finds portable tools more flexible than stationary shop tools. He can use them in the attic, out in the yard, in the garage, the cellar, in the hall closet, or wherever his labor is demanded. In addition, they do not require elaborate setups and they give him much greater use of the time that he has for the job. The biggest advantage is better workmanship.

2 ≡ ELECTRIC DRILLS
ARE FIRST

Drilling holes is a basic operation. One of the earliest power tools invented and certainly the most popular today is the electric portable drill. The hand drill was more than likely the first tool adapted to portable power uses. The job of drilling holes in various types of material is not only basic but is the task most frequently encountered in both woodworking and metalworking. Holes are needed for most of the devices used to fasten materials together. Bolts, cap screws, rivets, dowels, studs, wood screws, and nails all require some kind of a hole to fulfill their function as fasteners.

Electric power drills were developed primarily to do the job of drilling holes. The principle of turning tools and materials in a fast, rotary motion was found to be so useful and adaptable that a great many accessory devices were invented to be used with the hand drill. These additional applications and functions will be covered in a later chapter of this book. In this chapter we are concerned solely with the function of drilling holes with the portable power drill.

In all cases of holes drilled to receive fasteners and sometimes other parts of an assembly, the job must be done accurately. The hole must be of proper size, depth, angle, and

15

tolerance in order to provide accurate fitting for the fastener. If the hole is not drilled cleanly and accurately, the device will not fit properly and the work will be defective. Loose and inaccurate assembly may cause structural twisting, misfitting of other parts, or may even cause the fastener to be sheared off or pulled loose by uneven stress on the parts. Electric power drills not only make these necessary holes much faster than can be done with the ordinary hand drill, but they can make them more accurately and cleanly if the tool is properly handled.

Features to look for in a good drill. Illustrated here are two of the basic types of electric drills which are designed and built to meet the most rigid requirements of every craft that requires drills. In general, the over-all case of the drill must be neat and streamlined, rugged and of professional quality in appearance. The small, ¼-inch drill should weigh not over 3½ pounds and the larger ½-inch drill should weigh not over 10 pounds to meet the demands for easy handling and convenience in use. Above all, the design and shape should be such that the drill can be used easily in small and confined spaces. The tool must look as though it will do the job you want it to do.

After satisfying yourself as to the general appearance and design and the weight and feel of the tool in your hands, take a look at the other important features. The motor must be a rugged Universal type, AC-DC, 115 volts, designed for intermittent operation and equal to the job for which it is recommended. The idle-speed rpm (revolutions per minute) of the small, ¼-inch drill should be around 2000. That of the larger, ½-inch drill should be about 450 rpm. The motor should be equipped with compound reduction gears in order to deliver maximum power to the spindle. The gear housing must be readily accessible and equipped with grease seals so that it doesn't leak when heated up under operation. Spindle bearings should be a precision ball type to absorb radial and end thrust. The motor bearing should be of oil-less bronze. The commu-

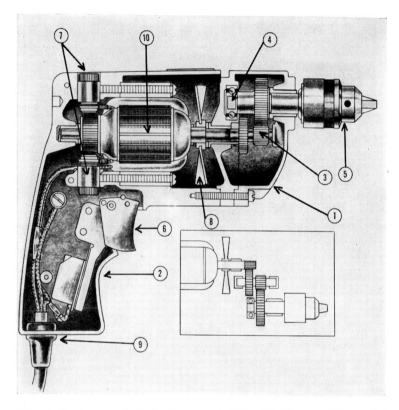

Fig. 4. Features to look for in a good drill. (1) Strong, lightweight case. (2) Convenient pistol-grip handle. (3) Compound reduction gears. (4) Spindle ball bearings. (5) Jacobs 3-jaw chuck. (6) Trigger-finger switch. (7) Accessible brushes. (8) Cooling fan and air ports. (9) Firmly attached safety cord. (10) Powerful Universal motor that does not overheat.

tator and brushes of the motor should be readily accessible for frequent inspection and brush changes.

Other features of the first-class electric drill include the three-jaw chuck which holds the drill bits, the handle, switch, and location of the connecting electric cord. The chuck should be the Jacobs gear type which has long been noted for its superior gripping qualities. Incidentally, it is the largest size capacity of the chuck which gives the drill its designation. The $\frac{1}{4}$-inch drill will hold bits up to $\frac{1}{4}$ inch in diameter in the chuck jaws. The $\frac{1}{2}$-inch drill will hold all the small ones and others up to $\frac{1}{2}$ inch in diameter. The handle of the smaller drill should be the pistol grip type and should give a full-hand grip to the user to provide maximum control and easy handling. In the case of the larger drill, an auxiliary handle is needed on the opposite side of the case to provide for two-hand control. This additional handle allows greater pressure when needed and also affords maximum control against twisting of the drill in the hole. A rear handle on the case is especially convenient for many types of drilling jobs and it should be adjustable for vertical or horizontal positions and removable for close work in crowded places.

The trigger or switch on the electric drill should be conveniently located at the base of the pistol-grip handle for quick finger control. This is absolutely necessary for accurate operation as well as safety. In addition to the trigger switch, there should be a push-button locking device located so that it can be instantly used or released by the thumb or side of the finger and located where it cannot be accidentally engaged. The locking button is a great help in one-hand operations. The connecting cord, which is usually about 8 feet long, should enter the machine case through the extreme end of the pistol-grip handle. This helps to keep the cord clear of the working end of the tool and out of the way of the operator.

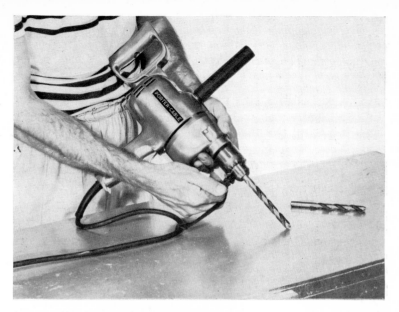

Fig. 5. *Top:* The three-jaw chuck must be tightened at all three openings to center the drill. *Bottom:* The extra handle on the larger drill is movable for various types of work.

Twist drills and bits for the electric drill. The drills or bits most often used in electric drills are called twist drills. Wood augers, screwdriver bits, reamers, and small abrasive bits are other accessory tools which are usually held in the drill chuck. The twist drill is the most commonly used tool and deserves considerable attention because it is also the most commonly misused and abused tool in the workshop. Furthermore, while these small and trivial-looking tools are considered "expendable" or "perishable" by shop bookkeepers, they are expensive to buy and must be in perfect condition to work properly.

Twist drills are made of either carbon or high-speed steel. High-speed drills are made expressly for work on metal and can take considerable heat without weakening the metal or becoming dull. Ordinarily, high-speed drills can do their work without the use of a coolant. The carbon steel drills are softer and are used solely on wood and soft metals or plastics. They cost much less than the harder steel drills but will wear quickly and become distorted if overworked. On soft metals, they require a flow of water, oil, or other cooling liquid on the tip to prevent burning. Never put water or other liquids on the electric drill. When it is necessary to work without a flow of coolant into the hole, the drill must be withdrawn frequently and dipped into a bath of cold water. Do not cool a high-speed drill bit in this manner or it is likely to crack.

Here is a rough guide for drill speed and coolant for various materials encountered in the shop ($\frac{1}{4}$-inch to $\frac{1}{2}$-inch drills):

> hard steel—turpentine and speed of 450 rpm
> machine steel—soluble oil and 450 to 800 rpm
> wrought iron—lard oil and about 1500 rpm
> brass—paraffin or a dry hole at 1500 rpm or more
> aluminum—kerosene is good at a speed of 2000 rpm

Straight-shank carbon drill, letter size.

Straight-shank high-speed drill, wire-gage size.

High-speed automotive drill.

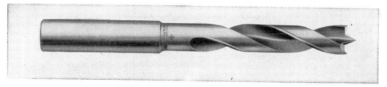

Machine bit for wood boring.

Short high-speed screw machine drill.

Fig. 6. Twist bits for the electric drill.

Lucite or Plexiglass—work dry at speeds over 1500 rpm
hardwood and softwood—no coolant and any speed

Since portable drills do not have adjustable speeds, these requirements indicate the type of work your drills will handle.
If your drill operates between the speeds for any two materials,
it will handle either of them.

The twist drill has no spur or screw at its end to pull it into
the work. It cuts away the material at the bottom of the hole
as the drill is pushed into the work while turning very rapidly.
Naturally, the most attention must be given the condition of
the tip of the drill. Dull and broken tips heat very rapidly and
will not cut straight, clean holes.

Wood auger bits with straight shanks are satisfactory for
drilling larger holes in wood with the electric drill.

Whatever type of drill or bit is used, never use anything but
one that is perfectly sharpened and in good condition. See the
chapter on sharpening tools for some good tips on taking care
of twist drills and bits and keeping them sharp.

Drill sizes are denoted by three different systems. The smallest drills are numbered according to wire-gage sizes from 1 to

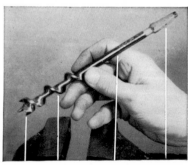

Spur Twist   Shank   Tang   Feed screw   Cutting edge

Fig. 7. The auger bit.

60, the largest being number 1, which is .228 inch in diameter. Number 60 measures .040 inch in diameter. Letter-size twist drills are commonly known as jobbers drills and range in actual size from A, which is .234 to the letter Z, .413 inch. The third series of twist drills overlaps the other two, but without duplication. The latter are in fractional sizes, increasing by 64ths of an inch from $\frac{1}{16}$ to $\frac{1}{2}$ inch. Straight shank and straight fluted drills for wood and soft metal are made in sets of 16 sizes from $\frac{1}{32}$ to $\frac{1}{2}$ inch. It is usually necessary to have a complete set of twist drills on the workbench. For the average workman, the set of fractional size drills does very well. They should be kept in a drill stand, however, so that the correct size can be readily selected. Inexpensive drill stands are available which have the sizes marked alongside each hole.

Correct technique for using the drill. Drilling holes accurately in metal, wood, or plastic is a simple operation if you have a good and dependable portable electric drill and the twist drill is sharp and in good condition. Some preparation and preliminary precautions are necessary, however, to guarantee good work. The three most important things to check are: (1) the work is securely fastened, (2) the chuck is tightened on the twist drill, and (3) the position of the hole has been clearly marked so that the start will be accurate.

Naturally, you have checked, first of all, to make sure that you have the right size drill. If there is any doubt, study the table of twist drill sizes and check the diameter of the fastener you are going to use. If the hole is being drilled for a wood screw, look at the table of screw sizes and select the right drill. Both tables are in the back of this book. Assuming also that your twist drill is sharp and accurately tipped, locate the exact spot where the hole is to be made and make a punch mark at that spot with the center punch. This small dent will prevent the drill from "walking" around the mark as it starts into the material.

Next, open the chuck of the drill and insert the twist drill fully into the jaws. Turn the sleeve of the chuck until the jaws grip the tool. Then insert the key into each of three holes and gear the jaws tight to assure concentricity. Make sure that it is tight. Place the tip of the drill in the tiny center tap and hold the machine firmly in position. Start the drill and you are on your way. Your first finger should be extended along the body of the drill to help guide the direction.

Above all, let the speed of the drill do the work. Keep a steady and even pressure on the bit, but only enough to keep the tip cutting. If too much pressure is applied, the tip will dull quickly and, with the smaller sizes, you are quite likely to bend or even break the twist drill. In either case, the hole will be imperfect and you may spoil the work. If the bit bends, the sides of the drill will enlarge the diameter of the hole. When the hole is to go through the material, ease up on the pressure as you approach the other side. Let the bit cut its way through instead of breaking out of the other side. Don't allow the drill to go any farther than necessary in finishing the hole. Keep it turning as it is withdrawn. It is at this breakthrough stage that the bit is most likely to jam and break.

Some workmen prefer to have less pitch at the point of drills used for hardwoods. Slower speeds of both drills and bits generate less heat and make a smoother cut in hardwoods. Softwoods should never be drilled too rapidly because of the tendency to tear rather than cut the fibers.

Never hold the work in your lap, or hands, or against your chest while using any kind of drill. Remember that the electric drill works many times faster than the ordinary hand drill. Fasten the work securely in a vise or clamp it to the worktable or sawhorse before starting to drill. Make sure that

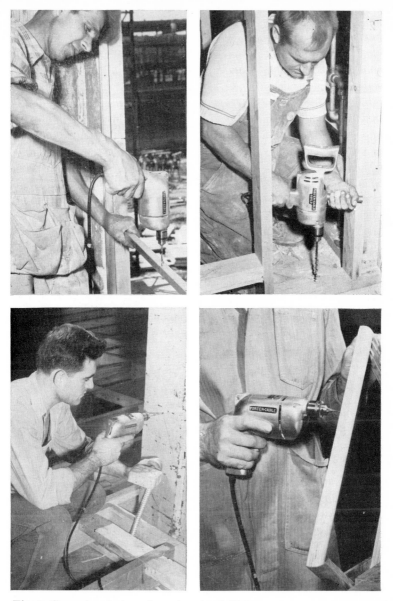

Fig. 8. Correct technique for using the drill demands a steady support for the work, a straight approach to the hole, and a firm, steady pressure.

the material isn't going to go flying around if the twist drill should jam in the hole. Unless the work is rather large and heavy, holding it with the foot is not a trustworthy procedure.

There are several methods for gaging the depth of a hole that is not to go through the material. A short piece of copper tubing slipped over the drill bit or a piece of scrap wood can be used for the same purpose to expose only enough of the drill to make the correct depth of hole. Or a short rubber band or piece of string can be fastened around the drill to mark the depth.

When thin material is to be drilled, back it up with a piece of scrap wood so that the twist drill will have a good bed to go into. Otherwise the material may be pushed out of shape and the hole will not be accurate. When drilling deep holes in wood, lift the bit partly out of the hole several times. This will clear the chips from the flutes of the drill bit and greatly speed up the work. It will also aid in making the hole more exactly to size.

To be sure that the drill is at right angles to the material, hold a try square against the surface of the material and square it against two sides of the motor housing.

The vertical drill stand. This is not an accessory in the usual sense of the word but is a highly useful piece of shop equipment especially designed for the portable electric drill. You can multiply the use and accuracy of your ¼-inch drill many times over with the vertical drill stand. It is a simple and inexpensive device, but precisely built for continuous and workmanlike service. The stand is built on a casting which forms the base and uses a polished vertical rod to hold the tool bracket. There is a vertical adjustment on the carrier for different thicknesses of work. The range of adjustment is zero to 7 inches. The maximum feed of the twist drill is 2⅝ inches.

The base has a drilling radius of 5⅜ inches from the center line of the column.

With the vertical drill stand fastened to the workbench, the operator can apply a steady and powerful pressure under exact control. With the electric drill clamped in the carrier, there can be no side movement or wavering of the tool from an upright 90-degree position to the work. Using the leverage of the handle, the feed of the bit can be controlled to a very fine degree. This is an exceptionally good tool to use with the portable drill for it can be fastened in a convenient location in the shop and the drill case inserted or removed in a few seconds. No tools are necessary to make the adaptation.

The drill stand is also useful for drilling holes in large sheets of wood or metal. The drill is turned away from the base and the base is weighted to hold the device in place on top of the material.

Special drilling jobs for the portable drill. Ordinary steel bits would be ruined very quickly in stone, cement, brick, cinder block, and such dense materials. For making holes in this type of material, use the carbide-tipped masonry drill bits that are especially designed for such work. Even when using these hard-tipped bits, however, care must be taken to prevent breaking or dulling the tip. Quite the opposite treatment from that given to ordinary twist drills is the advice for using carbide-tipped drills. Keep the pressure steady and increasing as the bit enters the work. Do not let the drill ease up or run idly in the hole. Once the hole is started, increase the pressure as the bit cuts away at the material. If you should get tired, pull it out of the hole for a minute, but don't let up on the pressure while the drill is working. Ordinarily, drill work in masonry and such material does not call for cooling liquids. If, however, the material is very hard and dense, a little water or turpentine will help keep the drill cool. If the problem of dust in the hole becomes serious, use an automobile tire pump to blow the dust out. When finished, be sure to clean out the drill thoroughly.

When you have the problem of drilling a series of holes at the same angle, make a jig from a piece of 2×4 and drill one hole through it at the correct angle. This block can then be clamped into position over the mark for starting each hole and, after the hole is started, the block can be removed for drilling to depth. Each hole will be at the same angle. When starting any hole at an angle to the surface, make a good, deep mark with the punch and start the drill into the material at a vertical position. When the tip has entered, change the angle of the machine to the desired angle for the hole.

Drilling holes for dowels often presents a problem in lining up the opposite hole for fitting pieces together. This job can be greatly simplified by using a doweling jig or, with a little practice and careful figuring, a marking gage and dividers. A simple yet very effective method for marking the hole centers is to mark a center line and spacing marks on one of the pieces to be joined and driving a small brad into the material at each mark. Take the nippers and clip off the head of the brad, leaving about $\frac{1}{8}$ inch of the point standing. Now line up the pieces of material and press them together. The brad ends will make clean and distinct marks for the opposing holes. Pull out the brads and drill.

When any quantity of work is to be done—either a number of holes in one piece or several pieces of similar work—arrange the work so that all the holes of one size can be drilled at one time. This will speed up the work and also make for greater accuracy. If called for, perhaps a drill jig can be devised which will make all the holes uniform and precise. A piece of soft steel or hardwood with holes drilled at desired intervals will help accurate spacing and locating. Any piece which serves as a pattern in making duplicate holes will serve as a drill jig. Heavy cardboard or thin plywood will do very well for large areas.

What you need for drilling. Here is a quick summary of the drill necessities for various types of work. It is not intended to be accurate or complete because the final word is an individual matter of considerable range. This list is suggested solely to give you an idea of the type of tools needed.

WOODWORKING AND HOME REPAIRS. The ¼-inch drill is usually sufficient unless there is to be heavier work such as house alterations and large furniture projects. Along with the ¼-inch drill, a set of 10 or 12 fractional-size twist drills of high-speed steel. A few carbon-steel bits of the more common sizes can be used on wood. You should also have 6 wood bits up to 1 inch in diameter. You will have to have a bench drill holder for using some attachments and will most likely need the drill press stand. Later, perhaps, you will want to add sanding disks, polishing and buffing tools, and possibly a hole saw to your outfit.

FARM AND GENERAL USE. For light work such as one encounters around the home workshop, the small drill is sufficient. A good part of the work around a farm, however, calls for the ½-inch drill. Repairs to equipment and machinery, fencing, gates, barn doors, farm buildings, etc. often require holes for large bolts and studs. For top-quality performance and general all-around utility, the ½-inch drill shown in figure 5 is by far the best deal for the farm maintenance man.

BUILDERS AND BUILDING SERVICES. The range of work that requires dependable and adaptable drilling is nowhere greater than in the building field. Holes of all types are required, from the foundation layout to the hanging of doors and installation of equipment. Both the ¼-inch and the larger ½-inch sizes are necessary. Here is one field of work where the best equipment that can be obtained is almost an essential. Around construction projects, tools are subjected to greater abuse and undue wear than ordinary work in the shop. The case of the drill must be strong, the wiring must be grounded and there must be extra handles and other aids for accurate work. A wide choice of twist drill sizes and wood bits must also be on hand.

SCHOOL SHOP AND TRADE CLASSES. The $\frac{1}{4}$-inch drill is the ideal tool for the class group in wood and shop work. Several of them, in fact, are necessary so that everyone can have access to the speed and accuracy of the portable electric drill when needed. Many schools have found these light-weight drills a great advantage in speeding up the class work and making the projects more interesting as well as more professional in appearance. A complete set of twist drills should be available, with extras of the more commonly used sizes. An arbor adapter, wire brush, small grinding wheel, sanding disks, and buffer will make the drill an even greater utility in shop-work instruction. These accessories will be discussed in greater detail further on in this book.

Maintenance of the drill. No more important message could be given regarding the use of any tool than the simple advice: *Read the instructions carefully.* Your electric drill is simple to operate and is built for many years of trouble-free performance. Satisfactory results, personal safety, and good performance depend on your knowledge of your work and the tools you use. A few minutes spent in reading the manufacturer's instructions will save many headaches later on. If trouble should develop, by all means contact your nearest authorized dealer and have repairs made promptly. He is the only one who can make adequate and guaranteed repairs to your electric drills. It is up to you to keep the tool clean and free of dust and dirt.

GROUNDING. Be sure the machine case is grounded before you start the motor. Should a short circuit develop during operation, the ground connection will prevent a possible electric shock. The connecting cord to the machine is equipped with a third wire that is grounded to the case of the drill. If the end of this cord has a pin jack on it, the pin can be threaded into the screw hole of the wall outlet box. If you work with an extension cord, it may be easier to solder a battery clip to the ground connection. The clip can be quickly attached to a small pipe in the ground or to the end of the ground wire of the extension. Make sure that the other end of the extension is also grounded. Don't think that you have accomplished a ground by making only one connection. Follow it through until you find the actual ground contact. In shops and industrial plants, it is necessary to have a three-prong outlet and male plug for such connections. The third connection is grounded.

DRILL CHUCK. Always bottom the drill bit in the chuck. The chuck jaws must grip the shank fully and firmly so that the bit will be exactly centered. Use all three holes in the chuck body to tighten the jaws. Insert the chuck key in each hole in turn and tighten as much as possible. Use only the chuck key to tighten or loosen the chuck jaws.

LUBRICATION. The gear chamber of the drills illustrated here is packed at the factory with a sufficient amount of grease to last the life of the bearings. Two or three drops of a high-grade lubricating oil should be added to the commutator end bearings once a month through the oil hole in the top of the motor housing.

DRILL CARE. Make a standard practice of inspecting your twist drills when you buy new ones and make a periodic check of the old ones. Keep all drill bits in a drill rack or box holder and keep them in proper order. Pick each one up by the shank end and examine the condition of the cutting edge. Look directly at the point to determine whether the center is correct. Look at the lip of the drill and at the radial clearance. Inspect the shank to see whether it is dented or chewed to an extent that it will not center properly in the chuck. Finally, roll the drill bit across a smooth surface to determine whether it is bent. If repairs are required, do them at once so the drills will be in good shape when needed. In chapter 9 of this book, we will explain and show how to sharpen and care for your twist drills and bits.

Since care and repair of motors on all portable tools is very similar in all respects, instructions and advice are given in chapter 9. Be sure to follow the directions given there for repair and cleaning of the commutator and care of the brushes.

3 ≡ PORTABLE SAWS

Electric saws are big time-savers. A large part of the time-consuming work in carpentry, house building, and general wood shop work is in cutting large pieces of wood to size for the project. This task is also one of the most physically demanding of all the jobs the workman in these fields has to do. The modern portable electric saw now does the job quickly and easily—the latest model on the market will cut across a 1×10-inch plank in one-half second. While the hand-saw workman is picking up his saw, the job is done if this new work-saver is used. Time spent in prolonged cutting operations can now be cut to one-tenth or even less. In the cutting of joists, studs, and rafters for a house, one man can easily do the work of ten with an efficient, portable power saw.

In most operations where wood is involved, the accuracy of the sawing is of utmost importance. If a piece is cut unevenly or cut too short, it cannot be used without considerable alteration of the structure or the creation of an unsightly or weak member. The electric saw makes straight, accurate cuts in almost any type of material. With a little practice, the average person can operate the portable saw with far greater accuracy and precision than a skilled workman can handle his hand saw. This type of accuracy and workmanship is most necessary in working with wood.

General features of the portable saw. Sizes and prices of electric saws vary a great deal and there is probably no one size and type that will be fully satisfactory for all workers. The size of the saw is rated by the diameter of the circular blade that it uses. Since the blades of the saw are quickly interchangeable for cutting all kinds of material and for all kinds of cuts, there are no designations of the machine itself as there are with ordinary hand saws.

Electric saws range in size from the small 4-inch blade up to the heavy-duty 10- and 12-inch blades for construction work. The 8-inch size is probably the most popular and gen-

Fig. 9. The portable saw cuts from the near to the far edge and from the bottom of the board up.

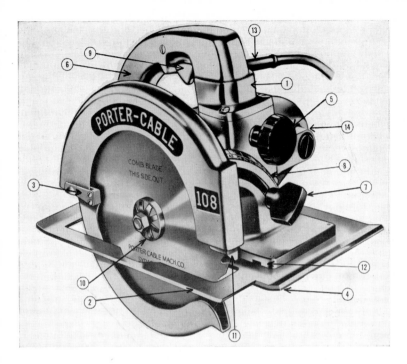

Fig. 10. Features to look for in a good portable saw. (1) Sturdy, light alloy case. (2) Substantial base of smooth, strong metal. (3) Telescoping blade guard with outside control lever. (4) A clear-view guide edge in front of blade. (5) A large hand-lock knob for depth adjustment. (6) Shaped and well-balanced handle. (7) Large thumb screw for sure-grip angle adjustment. (8) Clearly marked and accurate graduations on angle adjustment. (9) Snap finger-control switch. (10) Kick-proof slip clutch. (11) Automatic telescoping front blade guard. (12) Easily accessible and accurate holder for rip gage. (13) Sure-grip and out-of-way connecting cord. (14) Powerful Universal motor, AC-DC operating.

erally useful saw for home shop and general cutting operations. Since the general features of the saw shown here are similar to those of the other sizes, we shall discuss in detail the necessary requirements of a good portable saw which are illustrated in this model.

The motor is a powerful Universal, 115 volt, AC-DC, that runs at 4500 rpm load speed. The actual horsepower of such motors is not rated, but they should be about one hp for this type of saw. The frame of the machine is expertly designed for neat appearance and easy handling. The adjustments are instantly available and can be securely fastened on accurate settings of both depth and bevel of cut. It is quite important that the saw have helical gears for greater and smoother power and the elimination of "power jerk," or twist, when starting the motor. With the broad base, precision ball bearings, the helical gears, and well-balanced case, this saw is perfect for one-hand operation. It weighs only $13\frac{1}{2}$ pounds.

The depth adjustment on the 8-inch saw should be zero to $2\frac{3}{4}$ inches. On the larger saws, the adjustments range from a little over an inch minimum to $3\frac{3}{4}$ inches on the 10-inch saw and $4\frac{3}{8}$ inches on the 12-inch blade. These depth adjustments must be positively locked and easily released for altering the depth of cut. Other essential features shown on this saw are the safety guard over the lower part of the blade, which keeps the exposed area of the saw teeth at a minimum, and the large ports at the back of the upper blade cover for blowing saw dust away from the cutting line. The front part of the base is clearly marked for the rip gage adjustments and extends far enough out in front of the blade so that a marked line can be followed easily in free-hand cutting. The two small knurled screws on the front of the base allow a quick installing and adjustment of the rip gage and hold it firmly in place for ripping cuts.

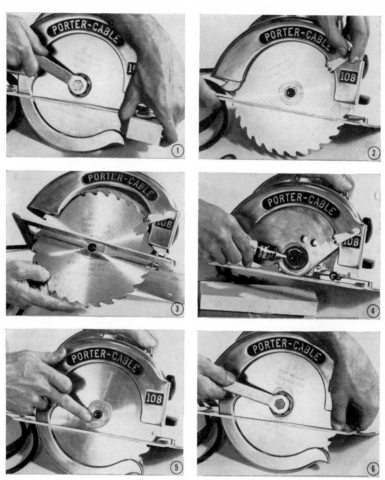

Fig. 11. Changing the portable saw blade. (1) Block the blade with a piece of wood and release the retaining screw. (2) Push the circular guard back until it stops in an open position. (3) Lift the old blade from the shaft and slide through bottom opening. (4) Clean the jackshaft face and add a film of grease; smooth with the finger. (5) Put the sharp blade in place and add a film of grease around the center. (6) Tighten the retaining screw while holding blade with fingers. Leave the clutch spring bowed out slightly.

One feature of this particular saw which is highly desirable is the kick-proof clutch of the blade installation. The saw blade retaining washer and the retaining screw assembly include a spring washer which allows the blade to slip if it should become bound in the cut. This friction-type clutch allows the motor to turn even though the blade is held stationary by the bind. This feature also smooths out the saw action, relieving motor strain and eliminating possible burn out of the motor. Also important, it protects the user from possible kickback of the saw and decreases the danger to gears and to the work on the table.

How to use the portable saw. The portable electric saw is a right-handed tool and is used very much like the hand saw. The difference is that the cut is made in the opposite direction, the blade cuts from bottom to top of the work and the speed of the machine does the cutting. Hold the saw with the right hand and the work with the left. Make sure that the work is safely supported and in a comfortable position for the person doing the sawing. The ideal height for sawing is about midway between the knees and the hips, or just below the hips. This height allows the body to lean forward and slightly over the work so that the guide line of the cut can be clearly seen. The height of the work should also be such that the worker can move the saw all the way across the width of the board without an extended reach.

Supporting the work properly is of considerable importance in any kind of sawing, but with the portable electric saw it is especially so. Work, or saw, horses make good supports and are about the right height for most ordinary sawing. Place them far enough apart so that the material has a solid support and place one of them close to the left of the line of the cut so the saw will not bind. The only thing to be careful of here is leaving enough clearance so that the saw blade can complete

Fig. 12. Good technique for using the portable saw. All pictures show the correct way to hold the saw, support the work, place the guide, and keep the blade clear of the sawhorse or work table. (1) Rip sawing with the rip gage. (2) Bevel cut with the angle gage. (3) Close-up of the compound miter cut. (4) A simple miter cut. (5) Close-up showing the blade cutting to the line and the guide edge directly above the mark. (6) Close-up of the compound miter, showing the full angle and the guide edge slightly beyond the mark.

the cut without sawing the support. When plywood or other light material is to be sawed, it will help considerably to place the stock on the table with scrap 1×2 material used to space it from the table surface. If you allow the blade less than 1 inch clearance below the material, the saw will easily clear the top of the table and will have a solid support to ride on.

The combination blade should be used for sawing plywood, particularly that over $\frac{1}{2}$ inch in thickness, because, with the grain running in both directions, you are both cross cutting and ripping at the same time. For thin plywoods, the small blade with very small combination teeth should be used. This gives a smooth edge without tearing the thin layers.

Always use the blade best suited to the type of work. For general cross cutting and ripping, the combination blade is quite satisfactory. If you have extensive sawing to do of any one type, change to the right blade. The cross-cut blade is more ideally suited to direct cutting action across the grain of wood and the planer blade will give an even better finish to the cut. The ripping blade will work somewhat faster and give a better cut on most ripping operations. These blades are known as specialty blades and at least one of each should be in every saw kit. You should always have an extra combination blade on hand so that you can change to a sharp blade.

When working up to about 35 feet from the outlet, you can connect the machine cord to a floor outlet or an extension of No. 14 wire. For greater distances, use a No. 12 or a No. 10 wire and connect at the fuse box. Lack of amperage will cause an overload that will lead to motor failure. Be sure, also, that the ground-wire clip is connected to a ground outlet. A good connection that you can be sure of is a convenient water or electric conduit or a pipe or rod driven into the ground near enough so that the clip at the end of the motor cord can be attached to it. Keep the inlet and outlet air passage on the saw clean and free of sawdust to keep the machine running at normal temperature.

Cross-cutting operations. Cross cutting may be done with the combination blade for ordinary work or with the cross-cut blade for a finer cut or with the planer blade if a really smooth edge is desired. In any case, be sure the blade is sharp and adjust the depth of the slide so that the blade just cuts through the work. On very thin or very thick materials, the depth adjustment is important in order to prevent any tendency to kick and to obtain a smoother cut.

Whenever possible, place the board to be cut so that the mark is at the right of the support. You should always cut on the right side of the line and lay out the work so that the saw base plate will be on the supported side of the material. Rest the front of the saw base on the work so that the guide mark lines up with the saw blade. Keep the blade well back of the work and start the motor, letting the blade obtain a full speed. Advance the saw steadily through the work, following the cutting mark with the guide at the bevel edge of the front plate. When you reach the end of the cut, release the trigger switch and allow the blade to follow through as the machine is lifted out and away from the work. Do not allow the blade to keep running or twist the machine at the end of the cut or the work can be badly scored. To prevent any sudden jamming or binding of the blade as you reach the center of the cut in a wide board, insert the tip of a screwdriver or any small wedge in the kerf at the near end. This will keep the cut open as the saw moves across.

There are several types of cross-cut gages and guides that can be used for various sawing and these will be discussed in the next chapter. As you acquire some experience with your portable power saw you will find that free-hand cutting across the board is quite easy and can be very accurate. One of the most important factors in obtaining this accuracy is the manner in which the saw is held. Let the saw balance itself in the hand. Get to know the feel of the movement required to keep the blade cutting. Never push or force the blade into the work. Let it cut easily and at good speed. Hold the machine firmly in the grasp, but let the grip be relaxed. Let the saw do the cutting, with your arm merely guiding and feeding the material as it moves across the board.

Rip sawing. Ripping can be done with the combination blade or the ripping blade. The latter will give a much smoother edge. Adjust the blade depth slightly more than normally used in cross cutting. Attach the rip gage and set the knurled thumb screw so that the gage will give the proper distance to the blade, and start the motor as in the cross-cut operation.

Generally, a slightly different type of arrangement for holding the work will be needed in ripping. One must be careful not to cut toward the saw horse or other support without making sure of clearance underneath. Ripping a wide board presents few difficulties because there is room to allow a good support for the saw and a good hold-down with the left hand. Place the board so that a cut can be run out to the limit of a reasonable reach. Release the trigger, but be careful that the saw is not moved. Now slide the board toward you so that the cut can be extended farther and insert a small wedge in the cut to hold it open. When you reach a point somewhere beyond the middle, it may be necessary to move the board down to the other end to complete the cut and allow a good support for the work. When cutting narrow pieces, it is usually necessary to use a straight edge and some kind of clamping device to make a secure base for the saw. Some of these devices will be described in the next chapter.

Of particular importance in rip sawing is the matter of kerf, or width of the cut made by the blade. The teeth of the saw blade are set at opposing angles to each other and remove material to a width about twice the thickness of the blade. This loss of material can be very important if the cut should be made on the inside of the line, that is, on the "good" side of the mark. The resulting piece of lumber would be short by $\frac{3}{16}$ inch. In all types of sawing, this difference must be remembered, although it will not be quite so critical in framing and heavy work. When ripping a piece of wood, be sure that you have figured out which piece you want to use, set the gage or straightedge so that the cut will be on the "right" side of the mark. The best method of making the rip cut accurately is to make the settings and place the saw against the guide so that the blade touches the wood. Lean over and look at it carefully from the front so you can see where the blade will enter the wood. Do this without starting the motor. When you are pretty sure that the cut will be exactly alongside the mark, turn on the motor and make a start so that the blade cuts about $\frac{1}{4}$ inch into the wood. Take the saw back and make a final check before going ahead.

Bevel sawing. Making a bevel cut with the portable saw requires a somewhat different approach. First of all, it must be remembered that the depth of cut possible with the saw set at bevel angle is not as great as that with a straight cut. When working at near-capacity limits, check the thickness first to make sure that the cut can be made in one pass. If it cannot, it may be best to decrease the depth so that about half the necessary depth is cut on the first pass. Then you can turn the piece over and complete the cut with a second pass. You must remember, however, to keep the same angle of blade on the opposite side and the bed of the saw will have to be guided along on the other side of the mark so that the two kerfs will be lined up. When you make bevel cuts, the saw must always be guided to the outside of the mark, or the long side of the bevel. Remember that the saw blade tilts under the base plate of the saw and the short side will be at the bottom of the cut.

Bevel cutting is sometimes confused with the mitering cut, which is actually an ordinary, straight-blade cut made at a 45-degree angle across the board. More care must be taken in starting the blade into this type of cut and the work must be held securely in place. A bevel cut that is made at an angle to the edge of the board is called a compound angular or compound miter cut and always requires a good mental picture of the finished result. Set the saw blade at the necessary angle and mark the long side of the bevel across the surface of the wood. It is a good plan, especially in the beginning, to make a trial cut with a piece of scrap and try the fit first. Once the

Fig. 13. The saw adjustments. (1) Depth slide lock. (2) Rip gage lock. (3) Angle segment lock.

angle and bevel are correct, the finish cut can be made accurately the first time.

Rabbeting and grooving cuts. With the portable electric saw, rabbeting and grooving cuts are made in the same manner as ordinary cross and rip cuts except that the depth adjustment is set so that the blade cuts only to the depth of the rabbet or groove. For either of these operations a gage or straightedge is a big help. Several passes may be necessary for wide grooves, but they can be made neatly and accurately if the extreme edges of the cut are clearly marked and each pass is accurately guided across the board. The second, or edge, cut of the rabbet will require another piece or a special setup for guiding and supporting the saw. Grooves, dadoes, and gains will be discussed in greater detail in the chapter on woodworking technique.

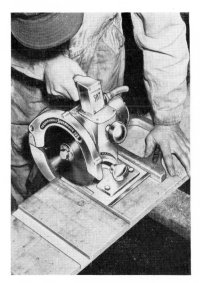

Fig. 14. Special jobs for the saw. *Left:* Cutting dadoes. *Right:* Pocket cut.

Pocket cuts. The pocket or interior cut is a frequently used operation for which the portable saw is ideally suited. In fact, no other tool or method can make this type of cut as easily and neatly as the portable saw. These are cuts which have to be made in the middle area of a board or floor or wall rather than at the end or edge. The area to be cut out should be marked exactly to its corners and with good, clear lines on all sides. Start near the corner limit on one of the sides and set the saw down so that the front of the base is resting solidly on the floor and the blade rests on the waste side of the mark. Adjust the blade depth so that the teeth will just cut through the other side. If there should be sufficient clearance at the opposite side, greater depth will give a closer corner cut, but this is not often possible. The blade guard will have to be held back for this cut at the start, but once the blade is down on the material the guard will stay out of the way.

Start the blade a short distance out from the near corner and, with the front of the base to steady the machine on the floor and the blade lifted about $\frac{1}{2}$ inch away from the board, start the motor. Lower the saw into the wood until the base rests firmly on the board. Back up to the near corner and then go forward in the usual manner to the opposite corner. Do the other three sides and the pocket cut is complete. You may have to use a keyhole or hand saw to clean out the corners because the blade of the saw is round and if the cuts meet exactly at the top, they will not meet at the bottom of the cut.

What saw do you need? The saw you get will be determined largely by the depth of cut which its particular blade size will make. The little 6-inch saw will cut up to 2 inches in depth. Since standard 2×4 lumber measures only $1\frac{5}{8}$ inches in thickness, this saw will handle 2×4 stock very nicely. The bevel cut, however, will not quite reach through a 2×4. For light framing, general house building and repairs, and home workshop purposes, the 8-inch saw will be better suited. For construction work where heavier material is frequently encountered, the 10- or 12-inch saw will be necessary. Around the farm, the 8-inch saw is the most practical. Even though you need to cut heavy lumber that is thicker than the 2¾-inch limit of the 8-inch blade, the degree of exactness is such that the material can usually be turned over for the extra pass. The big advantage of this saw for farm work is its lightness, durability, and convenience in the great variety of cutting jobs that have to be done. In the school shop and vocational classes, the 6-inch saw is usually all that is needed. A larger blade is available on the table saw when thicker materials need cutting. The 6-inch portable is much the easier saw for young beginners to use and will easily handle the largest sawing jobs that they have to do.

Maintenance of the saw. We have already cautioned the new saw owner about using a No. 14 or larger extension, connecting to a wall outlet or switch box, grounding the connection, keeping the air passages clean, and always using a sharp blade. All these things are necessary for good saw operation and safety. Another reasonable caution that should always be observed is that of disconnecting the cord before attempting to change blades on the saw. A wrench for the saw retaining screw comes with the saw. Use this wrench when changing blades. Push the teeth of the blade against a piece of wood or table edge and release the screw assembly by turning counterclockwise. Always clean the jackshaft flange and retaining washer before putting the new blade in place. Before installing the blade, put a light film of bearing grease on the face of the flange and on the side of the washer that contacts the blade. Make sure that the teeth of the blade point forward and upward at the front of the machine.

Read the instructions for your machine very carefully and

keep them handy at all times. Do not attempt repairs or adjustments without consulting the manual. If difficulties develop which you do not understand or you need repairs which you cannot make, write to your dealer or authorized service agency recommended by the manufacturer. Incidentally, it is a good idea to have all your electric tools inspected regularly by your nearest authorized service station. Periodic inspection will keep the cost of tool maintenance at a minimum and assure you of having good service from them at all times.

GEARS. If it becomes necessary to remove the jackshaft assembly, remove the front guard, the saw blade, and the screws in the gear housing cover. Place a ¾-inch-thick wooden block on either side of the gear housing cover, then place the saw blade and nut on the jackshaft. By holding the shaft with a hex wrench and turning the nut with the open-end wrench, the assembly can be easily removed. Do not attempt to pry the housings apart with a screwdriver because you can easily damage the machined surfaces and cramp the parts.

LUBRICATION. Use only the special grease provided and recommended by the manufacturer of the saw. Fill the grease cup on the gear housing once a week if the saw is in continuous use. Once a month, add a small amount of grease to the armature commutator end bearing. This bearing is covered by the large head screw in the end of the motor housing. Lubrication at this point will reach all the ball bearings and gears. Be sparing with grease and oil on all electric machines. Too much grease will cause the bearings to run hot and the grease will be thinned out. At this stage, it can easily run into the motor and also splash and drip out onto your work. A drop of oil should occasionally be put on the pin hinge of the blade guard.

BLADES. After getting some experience with the portable saw, you will be able to recognize a dulling blade just as soon as it loses its clean, efficient sharpness. The saw will be slightly harder to push across the board and it will not make as smooth a cut as it once did. When the blade first shows signs of becoming dull, change it and have the old one sharpened immediately. If you wish to do the sharpening yourself, look at chapter 9 of this book where we show how this is done.

GENERAL CARE. Clean the whole saw frequently and be sure that the adjusting devices and slides are free of dirt and sawdust. Don't let the motor housing or vents become full and choked. Keep the saw in a case. This is a small investment which will pay big dividends in protecting such a valuable tool. The case will also keep the wrench, tube of grease, rip gage, extra blades, and other needed parts where you can always find them. Refer to the motor section in chapter 9 for notes on caring for the motor of the electric saw.

4 ≡ SPECIAL WORK
WITH THE PORTABLE SAW

Making the saw guides. When you are first learning to use the portable saw, it will help considerably to use the cross-cut gage or cut-off square illustrated here. An elaborate or expensive device is not necessary, but the manufacturer makes one which is also useful as a try square and for many layout jobs. It is made of an aluminum alloy and the arm that places the square exactly perpendicular to the edge of the board extends far enough to locate the exact position of the cut. You will find this type of square an excellent guide for all ordinary cutting where a true square and straight edge is wanted. You can make one for yourself if you need a longer guiding edge or one that will guide a straight cut at other than 90 degrees to the edge of the board.

To make a cut-off square, follow the steps shown in the illustration and be sure that the edges of the material are straight and the two principal pieces are joined at the correct angle. Make a simple one first for straight, 90-degree cuts. Use $\frac{1}{4}$-inch plywood or Masonite for the flat, triangular piece and 1×2-inch pine for the perpendicular edge on the underneath side. A short piece can be attached to the top on the long side of the triangle for holding the guide in place. The

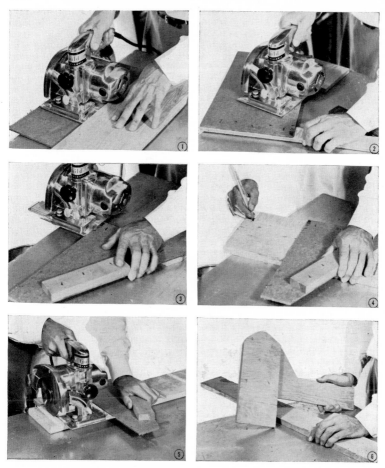

Fig. 15. Making a 90-degree cut-off square. (1) Cut a straight edge on a 10×16 piece of Masonite, using a straight guide. (2) Nail a guide strip underneath carefully at right angles to the edge just cut and cut the back of the triangle. (3) Fasten a holding piece along the back of the triangle, and cut off the foot piece. (4) Where the foot guide was cut is the indicator for all future sawing. (5) This guide can be used for any type of straight or angled cuts directly across. (6) Here is another type of guide with the squaring piece fastened at the top.

strip on the underside should extend out beyond the point where the saw will cut so that, when the guide is used the first time, the excess is cut off and the end will thereafter mark the exact cutting line of the blade. The one thing that you must keep in mind is that this guide has been cut for one particular saw. If you use more than one size, check to determine whether the base dimensions are the same before you use the guide on the other saw. It may be necessary to make a guide for each saw.

Another type of cross-cut guide can be made with the perpendicular aligning edge at the top. This one is particularly useful for handling small pieces of trim with the 4-inch or 6-inch saws. A similar guide will have to be made for each saw, however. No matter which type you make, be sure you use a very straight piece of stock to saw the perpendicular edges of the guide. You can cut the rest of the pieces using the edge guide on the base of the saw. Fasten the parts securely together with several small nails after locating them exactly perpendicular to each other by use of the carpenter's square or a good try square. Make the long piece that is to guide the saw about 14 or 18 inches long. This size will do for all widths of boards and most small sizes of plywood.

A longer and more elaborate square will be needed for making accurate cuts on large sheets of plywood, Masonite, etc. This frame can be made of straight-grained hardwood, but redwood is lighter, is straight grained, and is not likely to get out of shape by warping and twisting. Pick out a 6-foot piece that has a perfectly straight and smooth edge. Use 1×3-inch stock which you can rip accurately with the ripping gage and plane the edges smooth. The squaring piece that forms the base of the triangle should be no more than ¾-inch thick and at least 30 inches long. A large carpenter's square will help in locating the two principal pieces at a 90-degree angle. You might want to check further by using the right-triangle formula:

$$A^2 + B^2 = C^2$$

Measure a distance of 9 inches along the foot from the point of joining and a distance of 12 inches along the vertical side of the triangle. Make a distinct mark at the two points. If the angle is truly 90 degrees, the distance between the points will be exactly 15 inches. Leave the end of the footing piece

Fig. 16. The large saw guide for plywood. (1) Square the principal sides carefully before nailing. (2) Nail the top end back from the guide edge to clear saw. (3) Cut off the extending foot at the guide distance. (4) Squaring the guide to any edge, cut large sheets accurately.

just a bit longer, say 2 inches, than the width of the base of the saw. Nail the pieces together and brace them by joining the ends with a light strip on the side of the triangle away from the guide edge. Be sure that the pieces do not overlap at the top end to make a total thickness which will not go under the motor of the saw. Look at the photos and you can easily see the details for making this useful saw guide.

A saw protractor is now available which has a movable arm and graduated segment of full 180 degrees. It is readily adjustable to accurate settings by a thumbscrew which holds the saw guide firmly in place. This tool is more convenient for the carpenter and general shop worker than the fixed guides we've described. It can take off and duplicate any angle of cut and can be used with any size of saw because the arm does not extend out to the line of cut. This tool is also useful as an adjustable carpenter's square in laying out and measuring construction angles.

Sometimes it is necessary to use a longer straightedge than that afforded by the guides you have bought or made. When ripping a wide board, the cross-cut guides will not serve very well. In such cases, any straight piece which is thin enough to lie under the motor housing of the saw will serve very well. It can be clamped to the work or, if large enough, can be held in place by hand while the saw is guided along its edge. A handy guide can be made from a piece of Masonite and a strip nailed to it along the top of the left edge. This serves very well when ripping to a line because the saw rests on the base of the guide and holds it in place at the same time. Any convenient width of Masonite can be used because the saw will then cut off the excess and the edge will thereafter mark the line of the cut. The width of the base, from the guide strip out to the cutting line, will be exactly that of the saw for which it was made.

Fig. 17. Guides and jigs aid straight sawing. (1) The rip guide is held by the saw base. (2) End stop and clamps form table jig. (3) Cut-off square places all cuts alike.

Working with the saw guides. One of the best helps for shop work with the portable saw is a smooth table about 5 feet long, 20 inches wide, and 30 inches from the floor. This is a convenient height for using the saw and many setups can be quickly arranged with blocks and clamps for making different types of saw cuts. For instance, when ripping, the board to be cut is supported by scrap pieces of 1×2 or 2×4. The depth of the blade must be adjusted so that it will clear the table underneath the board. The rip gage or long guide can be used and the saw passed right across the supporting pieces. This arrangement gives the longest range of cutting without having to move and provide support for the work. Cross cuts and all types of angle cuts can be made right on the table if the work is supported by scrap pieces and arranged so that the sawing can be done without interference. Supports should be spaced so that there is no sag in the board and the weight of the saw will not cause the work to bend. These scrap supports are shown in use in the picture illustrating the table clamps.

Quite often it is necessary to cut several pieces the same length. This can be done very quickly on the saw table by arranging stops at the end and fastening them with clamps. In the illustration, such an arrangement is shown for duplicate cuts with the protractor guide. The stock material is pushed up against the stop at the end and alongside the parallel piece to the front. The end of this parallel stop serves as a locator for the guide. The saw will always cut at exactly the same place. Quick calculation can alter this arrangement for any length of board. This arrangement is a good one for cutting matching dadoes in the two ends of a cabinet or bookcase.

When working with the saw guides, particularly with those that mark the place of the cut, you will find that the wider blades, such as the combination, will saw the lower arm just a bit short and you must be careful of the exact measure from the guide to the kerf made by the saw blade. This is very important when making cuts for joints. When making exacting saw cuts with the guide, move the saw up to the material and sight the line of cut before starting the motor. After starting, move the saw in until the blade has barely touched the wood. Pull it back and see where the cut is starting before going ahead. It may be necessary to adjust the guide slightly to one side or the other.

Advanced work with the saw. So far we have covered the technique of making ordinary cuts with the portable saw by description and in pictures. These operations included rip sawing, cross cutting, angle sawing, beveling, mitering, and compound-miter sawing. While the same principles are involved, the portable saw does offer a few problems when it comes to making other types of cuts used in cabinet work, furniture, some building construction, and interior finish work. Many types of "helpers" can be devised to meet these problems and, with some experience, the saw user will be able to work out an answer to any type of sawing problem with his portable saw.

A definition of terms will help at this point. A *groove* is any cut-out section on either edge or face of the material, such as you commonly find on the edge of flooring or house siding. This is the *female* side of the tongue and groove joint. The opposite, or *male*, side of this joint is called the tongue. Flooring and siding stock is usually machined with the tongue on one edge and the groove on the other so that succeeding pieces fit one into the other. When a groove is cut across the grain of the material, or across the short dimension, it is called a *dado*. *Ploughing* is the process of cutting the groove lengthwise of the grain, or along the long dimension. A *rabbet* is a cut-out section along the edge of the material, on either or both of the dimensions. A dado that is cut only part way across or for only a short section along the edge or face is called a *gain*.

In chapter 10 of this book there is an illustration showing various types of common woodworking joints. Many of the joints shown are combinations or variations of the cuts described above. All of the straight cuts used in making the common joints, as well as the dadoes, rabbets, gains, and grooves can be made with the portable saw; and the cross-cut guide or angle gage should always be used for accuracy. In the illustration shown here you will see how the saw is used on the table to cut a simple dado for engaging a shelf. Several passes are made with the saw, with care to cut inside the edge marks. Do not try to clean out the cut with the saw, but use a wide and sharp chisel to remove the slender standing pieces that remain. If necessary, one or two strokes with a flat wood file will smooth the bottom of the cut to perfection. Lap joints and rabbets are made in the same manner, but the longer guide is necessary for rabbets that reach beyond the arm of the cross-cut guide.

When making these cuts, do not try to remove all the material with the saw, but leave at least $\frac{1}{16}$ inch of stock on each side of the blade with each pass. If there is no wood on one side of the blade, the saw will pull to that side. Another good practice is that of using only very sharp blades for fine joinery work. Either the cross-cut or the planer blade will give very smooth edges to the cuts.

By examining the illustrations of the joints shown in chapter 10, you will find several parts of joints that can be made with the portable saw. For instance, all of the lap joints, half laps, rabbets, and dadoes can be cut with the saw, and the tenon half of the mortise and tenon joint can be worked this way. The mortise side must be cut with an auger or drill and hand chisel or router, if the joint is large

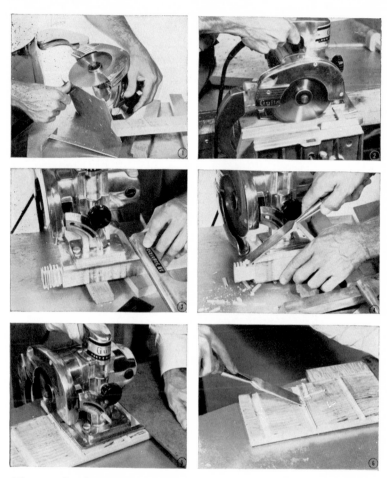

Fig. 18. Cutting common joints with the saw. (1) Set the depth of blade carefully. (2) Use a support for narrow edges, such as the groove for a tongue and groove. (3) Several cuts on all sides for the tenon. (4) Clean the tenon with a chisel. (5) Make several passes for the dado. (6) Clean the dado with the chisel.

enough to admit its use. The tongue side of the tongue-and-groove joint is easily made with the saw. It is nothing more than a rabbet cut on each side of the edge, with the center ridge left standing. The matching groove for this joint can be cut with the saw if the board is made fast to a thicker piece of material which is used to support the base of the saw. The rip gage is attached to the base of the saw and the blade adjusted to the exact depth of the tongue. Care must be taken that the grooving is not wider than the tongue and the edge of the board must be exactly flush with the edge of the support piece. This arrangement is shown in the illustration.

Using the radial arm and saw table. Builders, farmers, cabinetmakers, and shop maintenance men will find the radial arm attachment for the portable saw a very helpful accessory. For fast production work, this device is hard to beat. It consists of a movable arm mounted on a steel frame, an adapter for holding the saw, a hardwood table, and accurate calibrations for setting the various positions of the saw. In addition to fast, accurate mitering (either straight or compound), cross cutting, beveling, ripping, or chamfering, this device can be quickly set for dadoing, ploughing, rabbeting, or grooving. All of these operations can be handled on the radial arm without the use of the various guides mentioned before. The four drawings illustrate clearly how the radial arm is used for such sawing operations. The retractable arm, which moves in and out with the saw, allows a clear view of the work at all times so that very close and accurate cutting is possible. The bracket can alter the position of the saw by a simple half turn of the handle so that cross-cut or ripping positions are quickly changed. The entire head and the adjustable hold-down arm can be altered to any new position—raised, lowered, or swung—with accurate and automatic indexing to a full 45 degrees, either right or left, or to 90 degrees for ripping. The model illustrated here has a 27-inch in-and-out movement.

The technique for using the radial arm arrangement is exactly the same as that described for the free-hand use of the portable saw with the exception of the movement of the material. The saw cuts and moves in exactly the same way except that the base and guides are removed and the entire machine is raised, lowered, or angled to suit the demands of the work. Since the arm is fixed, the material must be moved along the table to the cutting position. The abrasive wheels can be used

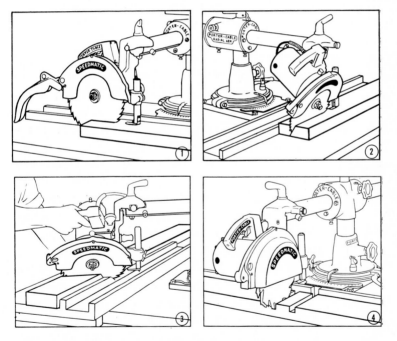

Fig. 19. Sawing with the radial arm. (1) Straight ripping cut. (2) Ripping at an angle. (3) The compound miter cut. (4) Position for either dado or cross cut.

with the radial arm for cutting tile, stone, slate, sheet metal, etc. in the same manner.

A light-weight rigid steel table is another portable saw accessory which is highly useful in the shop and for light work such as furniture making and cabinetmaking. The saw itself is attached to a holding device underneath the table top and the blade faces toward the front so that the cutting action is like that of a standard table saw. The blade guard, and the depth and bevel adjustments of the portable saw are utilized and the rip fence and angle gage of the table make possible a wide range of work and ample versatility for cabinetmaking, interior carpentry, and general shop sawing. The principal advantage of the table accessory is in being able to handle small pieces which cannot be accurately located or handled with the saw held in the hand. (See figure 2.)

Using the saw with the saw table introduces several other techniques and work possibilities that are difficult, if not impossible, with the portable saw held in the hand. Ripping, cross cutting, mitering, and making compound angular cuts are general operations which, by the use of the table fence and angle gage are easily done on the saw table. The procedure is the same as that previously described for the saw except that the work is fed into the blade and the blade cuts from the far side to the front and from the top of the wood down through the thickness. The guides enable the handling of smaller pieces and permit accurate work along the board edges and on the ends of joints and trim. A small piece of scrap should be notched on one end and used as a pusher stick to avoid getting the hands and fingers close to the blade when cutting thin or short pieces of material.

Rabbeting, grooving, and dadoing are all done in about the same manner as with the free-hand saw except that the rip fence and angle gage are used as the guides. Details for making these cuts are illustrated in chapter 10. Remember, when making dadoes and gains, that the blade is cutting on the lower side of the board. Always try the settings and the depth of cut on a scrap piece first to be sure the cut will be exactly where it is wanted.

Blades and special cutters. Previously we have mentioned the three basic types of blades which should be in every portable saw kit. If you examine the teeth of the cross-cut blade, you will find that they are made with a knifelike edge having a face bevel of 15 to 20 degrees and set alternately left and right. You will also notice that the filed surfaces of each tooth are always on the inside of the set. This angle of set and filing places the sharp cutting edge and points of the teeth on the outside of the blade. The teeth of the cross-cut blade have a knife action and sever the fibers of the wood.

The rip blade has flat-faced, chisel-like teeth which are designed especially for scooping out material lengthwise of the grain of the wood. Each of these blades cuts an especially smooth kerf when used in its proper field of operation and when it is properly set and sharpened. The combination blade has teeth that combine some of the characteristics of both ripping and cross-cutting blades and it does a very efficient job for each type of operation. When newly sharpened, the combination blade cuts a fairly smooth edge.

There are other fine-toothed blades that are designed for special types of work and that make an even finer cut than the cross and rip blades. The flooring blade is basically a cross-cut type and has very small teeth suited for smooth butt joints in hardwood flooring material. The planer blade has a combination of small cross-cut teeth with large ripping teeth, sometimes called rakers, cut behind every fourth tooth. This blade must be kept very sharp and it will do an extra-fine and smooth cutting job. Cross cuts and rips made with the planer need no further smoothing with the hand plane. Small and fine-toothed blades are also made for specialty cutting on Masonite, plywood, nonferrous sheet metals, and various types of wallboard.

Of fairly recent development are the carbide-tipped blades which are faced and set for combination cutting and which will outwear standard steel blades many times over. While these blades are much more expensive and cannot be sharpened in the home shop with ordinary files and stones, they do a remarkable job and give long-life performance on all types of building materials. The carbide-tipped blades will handle ordinary hardwoods, plywood, Masonite, Cemesto board, Transite, Formica, asbestos board, concrete form lumber, and many other such materials with equal facility. Care must be taken, as with all blades, that the sawing does not encounter nails or other hard objects, particularly when working on reclaimed or used lumber. Carbide-tipped blades are of particular advantage in general building work, knockdown or shipping rooms, heavy construction, factory maintenance work, and farm utility sawing. Various materials can be handled rapidly without the necessity for changing blades or frequent sharpening.

Cutting special materials. Your portable electric saw will cut cement blocks, fiber board, plastic, metal, siding and roofing materials, marble, and many other materials. The technique for making these cuts is exactly the same as that for cutting wood. One must be sure, however, to use an abrasive wheel or special blade for whatever material is being cut. With the special blades that are designed for concrete and other hard materials, care must be taken in starting the blade into the material. Sudden pushes or side pressure must be absolutely avoided because, even though these "blades" are tough and elastic, they can be cracked or broken. The new abrasive type of cutting wheels are practically unbreakable and produce excellent results. There is one type made for nonferrous metals

Fig. 20. Cutting hard materials with abrasive blades. *Top:* Cemesto board cuts as easily as wood. *Bottom:* Cutting through a 4-inch cast-iron soil pipe.

and composition materials, another for stone and plastic, and one for cutting iron and steel. Be sure that you use the right type of blade and you can have no trouble in cutting these tough materials. The caution on using grinding wheels under "Bench Grinders" in chapter 8 should be followed here too.

Useful devices for special jobs. With a little planning and some inventiveness, you can make a great many devices in the shop or right on the job which will speed up the work and make the portable saw increasingly useful. These are usually simple constructions made by clamping a few boards or blocks to a table so that the work can be quickly placed in correct position for cutting. In making sawing jigs and guides, it is a good idea to cut one piece first to serve as a pattern and set up the stops and guides so that subsequent cuts will make identical pieces.

Sawing duplicate lengths is not much of a problem if only a few are needed, but if the number runs to eight or more pieces, much time will be saved and the work will be more accurate if some time is spent in setting up the job. Use a bench top or a wide board placed across two sawhorses for the base. Tack a few scrap pieces of the same thickness (about ¾ inch) across the surface to provide saw clearance. At the left end of the bench, clamp or nail a block of greater thickness to serve as a stop for the material as it is pushed up to be cut. Place the sample piece against the stop and set up the saw and the cross-cut guide exactly where the cut needs to be made. Fix the position of the cross-cut guide by butting a strip against it on the left and alongside the edge of the sample, and fasten this strip to the bench. Cut the duplicate pieces by putting them in the position of the sample.

There are several other ways of doing the same job, some of which work better than the above method for short pieces. One type of overlapping guide can be used which is adaptable for many types of duplicate sawing. It combines the work support, a riser of thickness equal to that of the material being cut, and a piece of plywood nailed on top of the riser and extending across the work to serve as the saw guide. The stock being cut is slid underneath the plywood and against the riser.

When cutting studding or long duplicate lengths for a building job, whether it be a corn crib, feeding trough, or house framing, select a flat and level surface on which to set up the form. Lay out a number of pieces with ends against a straight backstop on the left, check the first one with the square and make sure that it is perpendicular to the stop. Nail it down and use it as a guide for layout and for cutting the other boards.

Ripping cuts can be made in much the same manner, using the same type of supports and stops. The long straightedge must locate the position of the cut correctly and, at the same time, serve as a guide for the saw. In all types of cutting, the one important thing to remember is the distance from each side of the saw base to the blade. If ever in doubt, make a block of plywood exactly the same size as the base plate and saw halfway through it in the position of the saw blade. With this piece, the saw mark and the guide and the stop positions can easily be checked for accuracy. A few models of saws have the blade outside of the base with no guide edge to the right of it. With such saws you can work only from the left edge.

5 ≡ SANDING AND FINISHING

Types of sanders and what they do. Three types of sanders are made, all of which have become quite popular and all of which are very useful tools for particular types of work. All three of these sanders are portable and each of them will do certain types of work more efficiently than any other tool. The rotary disk sander is usually one of the drill accessories and operates directly on the drill spindle in a rotary motion. This tool will be discussed more fully in the next chapter. The uses for rotary sanding are many and this tool, either as an accessory for the electric drill or as a "package" unit, will be found to be essential for many rough-smoothing jobs on wood, metal, auto, and general utility work. The abrasive for the rotary sander is in the form of a rigid or flexible disk, whichever is desired. The disk is held against a pad by a center screw arrangement. With the small electric drills, only the small 4- and 5-inch pads and disks should be used, otherwise the load of rough sanding will be too great for the motor of the drill.

The belt sander is probably the most important for general woodworking and is available in several sizes. These portable sanders use a continuous belt of abrasive which runs over a drive cylinder at each end of the tool. The belt runs across a flat shoe on the bottom of the machine. The abrasive action of the belt sander is all in one direction, from front to back of the machine. This gives a much more satisfactory action on grained materials and allows a smoother and more accurate method of working than does the rotary disk. Its greatest usefulness is on flat surfaces; although, by using a soft pad on the shoe, curved and irregular surfaces can be sanded. The belt sanders are all of the same basic principle in operation, but general features on the different sizes vary a great deal. As with the saws, the measurement of the cutting element determines the size of the tool. The width of the belt, from 2 inches to 4 inches, is the determining factor. Belt sanders are essential for all types of cabinetwork, furniture making, floor finishing, production-line work, and for finishing wall panels and door frames on construction and repair jobs. This is the heavy-duty tool where such sanding needs to be done.

The lighter finishing sanders operate with a tiny orbital motion causing the thousands of abrasive grains to move in $\frac{1}{4}$-inch circular orbits against the work at very high speed. This action gives a light, constant-speed motion which results in a very fine finish. With the proper grade of abrasive, the highest type of commercial finishes can be obtained with the orbital or finishing sanders. These tools are ideal for the school shop, fine cabinetwork, and interior finish work in carpentry. The tables of abrasives at the end of the book will show you what types and grades to use with the finishing sander.

What to look for in a good belt sander. A really good belt sander costs money and this tool is an investment which should not be lightly made. In speed of operation, neatness of work, and the professional quality of the job it will do, the sanders shown here are unexcelled. To anyone who has frequent sanding jobs to do, these tools will quickly pay for themselves in higher output and more satisfactory workmanship. Study these illustrations of sanders and know what to look for. As you read the description of the tool you can decide which type will best fit your needs. The three sizes shown will cover almost every type of sanding job that the belt sander can do and will show

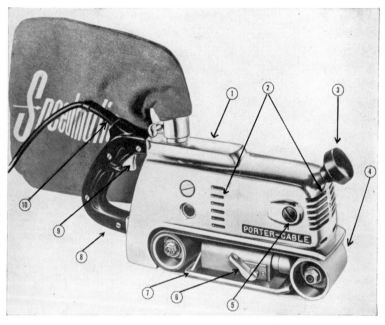

Fig. 21. What to look for in a belt sander. (1) A sturdy, neat case of lightweight metal. (2) Good vents for keeping motor cool. (3) A substantial and convenient front handle. (4) Rubber-covered traction wheel (back) and front wheel with good aligning adjustment. (5) Openings for motor brushes are easy to reach. (6) A positive spring-action belt tension release. (7) Solid and perfectly machined shoe base. (8) A solid handle that balances the machine easily. (9) Starting switch easy to reach and control. (10) The cord enters the machine where it doesn't interfere with the working parts.

you what features each size of sander must have to do its job satisfactorily.

The 2-inch sander is the lightest of the group, weighing only 9 pounds. This is enough weight to furnish a good cutting action without extra pressure and, at the same time, it makes the tool light enough to be used on ceilings and walls without great exertion. This precision-built machine works well on wood, metal, glass, ceramics, plastics, stone, and many other materials. All that is necessary for these varied operations is the selection of the right abrasive belt. The belts may be quickly changed for any degree of cut. The motor is a powerful Universal, 115 volt AC-DC, 0 to 60 cycle. Do not connect it to a 230-volt circuit.

The 3-inch belt sander is a little heavier, weighing 14 pounds. This is a heavier-duty tool running at 1000 surface feet per minute, about twice as fast as the 2-inch described above. The bearings are ball and needle for extra long wear and smooth running. The length of the belt is 24 inches, just 3 more than on the 2-inch sander, but the increased speed under normal load gives it much greater cutting action. This is an excellent machine for the general carpenter and builder as well as wood shop and class groups.

The 4-inch belt sander is the heavy-duty professional tool for millwork, building operations, furniture building, and cabinetwork. The belt size is 4 by 27 inches, giving a working surface of 25 square inches. The normal load speed is 1140 surface feet per minute, which gives an exceptionally good, fast, and uniform cutting action. The drive on this sander is a worm gear and chain transmission. The motor is 115 volt, AC-DC, 25 to 60 cycle single phase. Net weight of the tool is 25 pounds, which makes it exceptionally good for fast sanding on large surfaces. The vacuum system makes this sander a dustless tool.

These sanders have a highly polished aluminum alloy frame of very rugged construction. The chain case on the left rear side of the frame is neatly recessed and is completely enclosed. The cover can be easily removed, however, for maintenance inspection and greasing. There is a belt traction block of hardened steel located to the left and rear of the idler pulley and fastened to the frame with two screws. This block protects the frame when tracking the belt. The rubber-covered drive pulley is tapered from the center to either side to make the belt run true and in line with the idler pulley. This drive pulley is easily replaced when worn. The belt aligning screw is located on the left front of the machine and is turned to left or right to adjust the belt until it runs in the center of the pulley.

Operating the belt sander. Again, we repeat those well-chosen words of advice, "read the instructions." The manufacturer has designed a good tool that will do a real job for you. You are spending good money to get that service in your shop. Read the instructions thoroughly so that you will understand how to use and care for your investment. Lubricate only as directed and use the oil and grease that is recommended. In case of trouble, get in touch with your dealer or the nearest authorized service agent.

The first step in operating the belt sander is putting on the belt. Be sure you have the proper size for your machine and select the grit according to the material you are working on and the speed at which you wish to cut the surface. Later in this chapter we shall explain the uses of the various abrasive materials and grits. Retract the idler pulley to relieve the tension. On the two larger machines described before, this is done with a tension relief lever located just behind the front pulley. On the 2-inch belt sander, pressing the front pulley back will catch the release spring over a pin. Now look at the arrows printed on the inside of the belt. Hold the belt so that

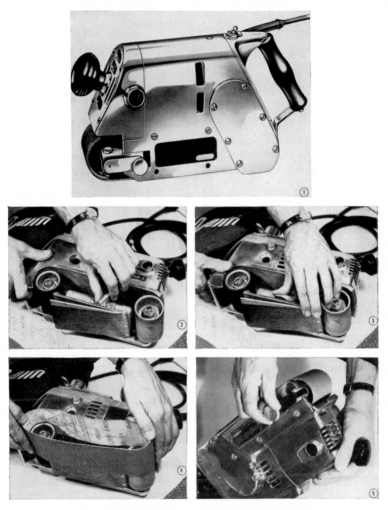

Fig. 22. (1) The lightweight 2-inch sander. (2) To install the belt, pull back on the tension lever. (3) Lock the lever behind the holding pin. (4) Start the belt over the rear wheel first, with the belt arrows pointing forward at the top. (5) After releasing the tension lever, start the motor and adjust the alignment.

the arrows point toward the front of the machine on the top and toward the rear on the bottom as the belt travels clockwise around the pulleys. Slip the belt over the pulleys and release the tension lever. Tilt the machine so that the belt will run free and start the motor. Adjust the aligning screw backward or forward until the belt runs in the center of the pulleys.

Be sure the switch is on the off position before making the connection to the outlet. Some belt sanders do not have a trigger switch like the saws. If the machine is "on" when the cord is plugged into the outlet, it will jump forward at a pretty rapid rate of speed. Make a habit of leaving the switch turned off. When you are ready to start work, connect the cord plug directly to a wall outlet or switch box and be sure to connect the ground wire to a ground, not to a false connection. If an extension is necessary, use a No. 14 wire up to 50 feet from the outlet.

Start and stop the sander off the work and apply it to the material only after the belt is running at top speed. Guide the tool over the work without using any additional pressure. The weight of the machine will do the job. To smooth a rough surface quickly, work diagonally across the grain with a rough or coarse abrasive. Always finish each working by a thorough going over with the grain until all the cross-grain marks are completely removed. Change to a finer grit and work only lengthwise of the grain, using full strokes and considerable overlap. A fine grit will give an extra smooth finish if worked carefully lengthwise of the grain on the third change of belt. Do not let the machine tilt while working on the flat surface and do not let it drop at the ends. These mistakes will cause deep cuts or rounded edges that are hard to correct. Keep only the flat surface of the belt working and use a light touch. Never try to rush the job. The belt sander will do it quickly enough. Overlap the strokes slightly and let the weight of the machine carry the load. All you have to do is guide it.

Taking care of belt sanders. In addition to having all your electric tools checked once a year by the service dealer, a few simple precautions and operating rules will make your belt sanders last much longer and continue to give top service. The motor is cooled by a fan which draws air in at the commutator

Fig. 23. Using the belt sander. (1) Work across grain on rough work. (2) Start and stop the motor off the work. (3) Close-up, showing the bench stand.

and expels it through the side ports in the frame. Keep these air passages clean and the dust blown out of the motor. Do this chore after every operation and during the long jobs. Check the motor following the suggestions in chapter 9.

Check the wear on the drive pulley occasionally and replace it when it becomes worn. To service the chain case, remove the cover and clean and repack with fresh chain-case grease. Use only the grease recommended by the manufacturer. Do this about every six months. Replace the chain when the links become sloppy on the pins. Put only a small amount of grease on the end ball bearing of the armature commutator.

Accessories for belt sanders. There are not many extra devices made for belt sanders, but some are very practical to have. A case, of course, will protect the tool, keep it dry and clean, and provide a handy container for the tool and necessary belts, wrench, grease, pads, and extras. The wrench and grease, as well as extra belts, should always be on hand wherever the sander is used.

A flexible pad is a very useful device for the belt sander. It fastens onto the base in place of the regular shoe and is secured by three screws at the front end. This pad has a soft rubber base which allows the sanding belt to conform to curved and irregular surfaces. It is used in exactly the same manner as the ordinary pad, but applied on slightly concave or convex surfaces.

The canvas belt is another useful accessory which is necessary for rubbing plastic or metal and for various types of varnish finishes. The canvas belt and the sewed felt belt are used with polishing rouge or other abrasive compounds for fine finishing and polishing. Do not use oil or other liquids on these belts. The rouge or compound is applied directly to the belt and used dry.

The bench stand assembly pictured here is a very good accessory for the belt sander, particularly when working on small sections. The sanding machine fastens to the rear edge of the table with two long screws and thus enables one to work small pieces which could not be handled accurately with the machine held in the hand. Fine precision work in making accurate edges and joints can be done with the bench stand arrangement and this device is one that should be in the cabinet shop as well as the vocational school shop. By using the front wheel of the sander, curved edges and close, inside parts can be effectively sanded with the bench stand setup. Belts can be changed quickly without removing the sander from the stand.

What to look for in a good finishing sander. There are about as many finishing sanders on the market as there are small electric drills. It is no wonder that the average buyer is utterly confused when he sees such an array of impressive-looking tools in the stores! Upon careful examination, however, and armed with some knowledge of what to look for, you will find that the field will narrow down quickly and considerably. Unfortunately, price again is not a good indicator of quality. Nor can the buyer always rely on the generous claims of the salesman he might meet. To get a good one, you have to know your sanders. Actually, finish sanders are all alike in many operating features and they will all hold some type of sandpaper material. We shall describe two different types of finishing sanders which will give you a good idea of how to judge the value of these tools.

Both of these sanders operate with an orbital motion, not a front-and-back vibrator movement. The orbital motion gives a much cleaner and faster cutting action which is important when working on large areas. Because this orbital motion sands with, across, and against the grain, all at the same time, it can smooth butt joints where the grain meets at right angles. This is one area where the orbital finishing sander is an advantage over the belt type. Both of these machines are ideally suited for coarse, medium, or fine sanding as well as rubbing and polishing on wood, plaster, metal, glass, and plastics. The working speed is many times faster than hand operations. Both of these machines are well balanced and light in weight. Standard 9×11-inch abrasive sheets divide exactly into three pieces to fit the pads of these sanders.

Special features of the light-weight sander include a gearless action belt drive which makes for smooth, continuous, and trouble-free operation and no oil leakage. The motor should be a ball bearing, Universal type, AC-DC, designed for intermittent light operation without overheating. It also should be a quiet running motor. The machine shown here is a simple, gearless design which gives nothing to get out of order. This sander weighs only 6 pounds, which makes it easy to use on vertical or overhead surfaces without fatigue. This particular sander has a unique, patented, paper clamp device which makes the installation of the abrasive sheet very easy and fast. The triangular clamps draw the paper in at each end, holding it taut over the pad.

Cool operation of the sander is accomplished by a large air intake, located high up on the machine and drawing in large quantities of clean air. The air exhausts at the bottom of the motor housing, blowing dust away from the work. The bearings of some sanders are permanently sealed and require no lubrication. This prevents the possibility of oil leaking out and spoiling the work. The trigger switch is located directly under the finger position on the handle.

The large finishing sander shown in the illustration is made for heavier work. The orbital motion of the larger machines is

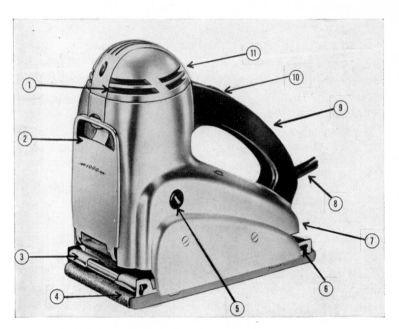

Fig. 24. What to look for in a good finish sander. (1) Good, open vents for keeping motor cool. (2) A smoothly designed case that is easy to keep clean. (3) Positive locking action for holding abrasive strips. (4) A large solid base that holds full strip of abrasive. (5) Brushes easily reached for inspection and replacement. (6) Smooth-acting movement of the base, describing small circle. (7) Balanced case which distributes weight evenly over the base. (8) Cord enters machine at end of handle and is out of the way. (9) Handle allows full grip and good control of machine. (10) Switch button easily reached by thumb or finger. (11) Case opens easily for cleaning motor and commutator.

slightly less than that of the smaller ones described before. The movement is about $\frac{3}{16}$ inch at a speed of 5000 cycles per minute. This action will give the finest finish possible and with minimum fatigue for the worker because the whole machine weighs only 8 pounds. Counterbalance in the construction of this tool cancels out the vibration, thus making it a one-hand operation. The switch on this machine is a thumb-operated sliding button on the top of the curved, plastic handle. The frame is a highly polished die-cast aluminum alloy of simple and efficient design.

Accessories for finishing sanders. A carrying case for each type of sander is recommended. A pad key and instructions come with each machine. For the larger machine, a flexible sponge-rubber pad is available which provides for sanding irregular, either concave or convex, surfaces. This additional pad is particularly useful for rounding the edges of plywood and trim lumber, furniture, store fixtures, school desks, and in many places on auto bodies. It must be stressed that these tools are finishing sanders and should be used only as such. They are not very efficient where large amounts of material have to be removed or deep scratches and dents have to be worked out. There are no other major accessories for these sanders.

Uses and application of finishing sanders. Finishing sanders take a very light cut and, in general, must be used only for those jobs which demand light smoothing and extra-fine finishing. Builders and carpenters use them for leveling taped wallboard joints, for smoothing plaster, for final cabinet and door finishing, and for final cleaning up work on built-in furniture. Woodworking shops find finishing sanders useful for all types of touch-up and cleaning work, leveling butt joints where the grain of the adjoining wood is perpendicular, and for rubbed finishes on furniture.

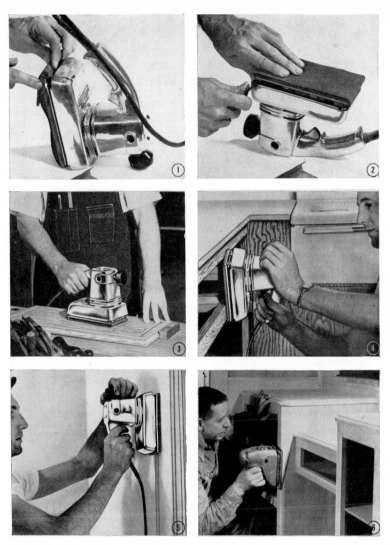

Fig. 25. Using the finish sander. (1) Insert the abrasive strip under the holding bar. (2) Turn key to take up slack in the strip. (3) Before assembly finish the parts with light strokes. (4) Put fine finish on facings after assembly. (5) Feather edge wallboard joints with slight pressure. (6) Using fine grit abrasive on prime coat makes better finish.

Display builders and window trimmers, sign painters and interior decorators find these sanders good for many light smoothing operations such as plywood cut-outs, plaster relief and ornamental work, joints and repairs made with wood putty, and for roughing surfaces to receive some types of lettering and stencil paints. Vocational schools and class workshops use them for many types of project work, especially on light materials, as well as for resurfacing blackboards and finish sanding on desks and tables.

Factory maintenance and production industries also find a wide variety of uses for finishing sanders. They work especially well on soft metal parts such as are used in the aircraft plants. On both castings and rolled metals, heavy duty sanders and grinders do the rough work of removing the bulk of the material. The finish sanders put on the smooth surface necessary for final polishing. They are also used for deburring edges on soft metal parts which have been stamped or sawed by machine and remove scratches and tool marks where they often appear on polished surfaces. The portability of the electric finish sanders is especially important around the plant. They can be used without the necessity for moving the material, often a costly and inconvenient process. Furthermore, when such work is found necessary, the small sanders can be taken right into the assembly where a large machine could not be used.

How to use finishing sanders. First, read the instructions in the operating manual which comes with the machine. Second, be sure the connecting cord is grounded. Third, be sure to use only the recommended voltage—the machines shown here are made for 115 volt operation. Always connect the cord to a wall socket or switch box outlet that has adequate wiring. Power tools require at least a No. 14 wire; and for long extensions a No. 12 wire should be used.

Attach the sanding pad before turning the machine on. Consult the table at the end of this book for selecting the right abrasive and insert one end of a $3\frac{2}{3} \times 9$-inch strip under the front or rear tumbler on the pad holder. Turn the tumbler with the key until the strip is caught. Do the same with the other end and draw the sanding strip up tight by working both ends as may be necessary.

These sanders are made for one-hand operation. Because of their light weight, perfect balance and absence of vibration, they can be guided over the work in any direction by one hand. The normal weight of the hand and arm is quite sufficient to perform sanding and finishing operations. Bearing down on the machine merely slows up the movement of the pad and decreases the efficiency of the abrasive. It also places an additional burden on the motor which will cause it to overheat. When sanding on vertical or overhead surfaces, use only enough pressure to hold the machine to the work, letting it operate at its full speed.

Finishing sanders operate best with garnet, aluminum oxide, or silicon carbide abrasives. Flint paper is entirely too soft for machine work and emery materials should be used only for cleaning and polishing metal parts. In general, cloth-backed abrasives last much longer and do a better job for almost all purposes. Whatever abrasive you use, always start with the coarsest grit necessary to reduce the high spots and excessively rough areas quickly. Use open-coat abrasives (this will be explained later on) and work the machine in all directions across the surface so that the sanding will leave an even surface. After a thorough clean-up with the coarse material, change to a finer grit and give the work another good going-over. A third and fourth change to successively finer grits may be necessary to get the desired finish. On most materials, however, two changes of grit will be found to be sufficient, particularly if the wood has been plane finished at the mill.

If the sander should start to jump around while working on a flat surface, it is probably due to the felt pad's not bearing evenly on the work. Remove the machine from the work and take off the abrasive. Place a sheet of 150 grit open-coat abrasive paper face up on a flat surface and run the pad on it until the felt is leveled. Bearing down too heavily may also cause the sander to jump. When working on metals, plastics, or painted or varnished surfaces, lubricants such as water, water-soluble oils, kerosene, or other noninflammable liquids may be used to cool the surface or to obtain smoother finishes. Always use a waterproof paper abrasive when using lubricants and wet the surface of the paper with a light film of the liquid. Be careful that water or other lubricants are not splashed or sprayed onto the motor or upper part of the housing. Never use inflammable liquids such as benzine, naphtha, or gasoline as lubricants with any electric tool. The motor sparking can quickly start a bad fire.

Maintenance of sanders. LUBRICATION. The armature shaft and eccentric assembly are usually fitted with sealed bearings which are prelubricated for the life of the bearings. It is not necessary to oil some sanders. The big machine shown in the illustration has one oil cup which acts for all the moving parts that need oil. The central reservoir is connected to the oiler fitting on the side of the machine. Add $\frac{1}{4}$ ounce of oil every week when using constantly and every two weeks when used intermittently.

GENERAL CARE. Keep your machine clean and free of dust accumulation. Keep it in the carry-all box or case when not in use. Keep it out of damp or oily places. Take reasonably sensible care of your sander and it will last for many years. If it is necessary to disassemble the machine either for inspection or cleaning, look over the instruction booklet first. Be sure that you understand what you are doing before you take the machine apart.

Abrasives for sanders. Machine sanding and hand sanding are different operations and produce different results. A particular grade of abrasive will produce a smoother finish when used on a machine, particularly the finishing sander. In the high-speed operations of machine sanding, ordinary sandpaper such as flint and garnet on paper backing do not stand up. The paper tears quickly and the abrasive grits work free of the backing in a hurry. All of the natural abrasive substances —emery, flint, garnet, and corundum—are prepared from stones found in the natural state. They do not stand up under high-speed machine work as well as "artificial" materials.

The principal abrasive materials in use today are the manufactured substances: silicon carbide and aluminum oxide. An open-coat garnet cloth abrasive can be used for finishing soft woods and wallboard. Silicon carbide (marketed as Carborundum or Crystolon) is an extremely hard substance and is used in the form of grinding wheels, cloth and paper-backed sheets, belts and rolls, stones, and many special shapes. As a wet-or-dry paper, it is especially useful with sanding machines for wet-sanding on lacquer or varnished surfaces, removing old paint or varnish, and for finishing floors. Aluminum oxide (sold as Alundum or Aloxite) is not as hard as the silicon carbide but is tougher. Wheels and disks made of this material are not as easily broken; and, in the form of sheets, it serves much better for sanding metals and other hard materials.

Generally speaking, abrasives are classed as open coating or closed coating. These terms mean that the spacing of the grits on the paper or cloth backing are either close together or somewhat apart. An open coating will allow the particles of wood or metal or other material being removed to jam between the grits and clog the paper. The closed coatings, however, provide a hard, fast-cutting surface for sanding hardwoods and the hard and dense metals. The open coatings are best for soft materials: soft metals, soft woods, and painted surfaces.

6 ≡ COMBO TOOLS AND DRILL KITS

The universal maid-of-all-work. No tool ever caught the public imagination and found such a great variety of jobs to do in such a short time as the small hand drill and its combination kits of accessories. This electric power tool has done more than run wild through the "gadget" field. It has made possible a great number of small jobs which simply could not be done in any other way. Now, in every hardware store, one will find different types of small $\frac{1}{4}$-inch drills in a special box fitted with table stand, grinders, sanding pads, abrasives, buffers, polishing heads, twist drills, small stones, wire brush, and possibly a sanding drum. Available nearby will be slitting saws, belt sanders, hole saws, carbon brushes, masonry drills, tire rasps, paint mixers, hedge trimmers, step pulleys, screwdrivers, metal shears, face plates for turning, knife sharpeners, polishing brushes, bayonet saws, countersinks, reciprocating sanders, grinding wheels, wood augers, paint scrubbers, drill stands, and a roto-hone. This list is not exaggerated but is copied from a manufacturer's leaflet advertising the "uses" of the little-dandy powerhouse drill.

Actual experience with all of these "gadgets" will convince the more serious worker that, like the beautiful fishing lures found in sporting goods stores, they are designed more "to catch the fisherman than the fish." Many of these inventions really work and serve a practical purpose. Many of them are just too light and impractical to be used for serious woodworking or construction purposes. Around the house, however, these small, portable kits have really found their place. They can polish silverware, furniture, automobiles, floors, golf clubs, tools, woodwork, and almost anything they can reach. When you buy one of the small drills, it is good economy and good sense to buy one of the better kits which include the drills, grinding wheel, adapter, pad, buffers, polishing heads, rouge, and sanding disks that you will need.

Specialized combo-tool kits. Pictured here are some of the newest and most practical kits typical of those which have been assembled for special purposes. Each of them is complete in a steel carrying case and is built around a new model $\frac{1}{4}$-inch drill. This particular drill is driven by a powerful Universal motor at 3000 rpm and weighs only 5 pounds, 13 ounces. The shop kit and the home kit should include a horizontal drill stand which converts the drill into a stationary bench grinder or polisher, the back-up pad and abrasive disks, buffing wheel, wire brush, 4-inch grinding wheel and rouge. Beyond that, each kit includes other accessories which make it especially useful for its intended purpose.

Other specialized kits are designed for the painter and floor finisher and for the garage and automobile body worker. The featheredge attachment (slip disk) found in the auto kit is a perfect tool for repairing paint jobs on automobiles or on furniture. All of these devices and special tools are interchangeable and can be added to whatever kit you might choose to start with. Furthermore, there are several additional accessories that can be purchased for general shop work.

The sanding drum unit, available as an extra accessory with

Fig. 26. The combo tool kits and accessories. (1) The home kit with extension handle. (2) The shop kit with drills. (3) Power take-off wheel. (4) The sanding drum accessory.

any of the kits, is a highly valuable addition to the combination-tool equipment. When the drill is held in the hand or fastened in the bench stand, this adaptation makes possible many types of sanding on curved edges and irregular contours that are not possible with other types of sanders. It is also used as a handy knife sharpener and metal deburring wheel.

The power take-off wheel is another useful accessory which attaches directly to the drive shaft of the motor. When the machine is attached to the table stand, the user can make the small drill into a powerful drive unit for a jig saw, small bench grinder, polishing wheel, or many other shop devices. Another accessory, the wheel adapter, which is included with both the home and shop kits, should not be confused with the power take-off wheel. This adapter unit is used to attach any wheel which does not thread directly onto the machine shaft, except for the 7-inch abrasive cutting wheel which attaches with a special metal hub.

The abrasive cutting wheel must not be confused with the sanding abrasive disks. The sanding disk, also 7 inches in diameter, is a new development in answer to the demand for a heavy-duty surfacer for hard, aggregate substances. It is similar to the cutting wheel in construction, but is somewhat thicker and is slightly flexible. Since the abrasive is impregnated into the fiber of the wheel with a waterproof plastic bond, water or other noninflammable liquids may be used as a cutting aid without fear of dissolving the bond. This wheel will score or surface stone, tile, brick, concrete, and other hard aggregates. It will also cut sheet metal and light bar stock as well as clean cement off tile and brick.

The usual chip hazards of grinding wheels are not present in the small 4-inch grinding wheel that comes with the home and shop kits. This wheel is for putting sharp edges on all cutting tools, either in the kitchen or in the factory. It is constructed of Carborundum-filled fiber which completely eliminates the possibility of the wheel's becoming chipped or broken. Furthermore, it does not remove metal as fast as the large stone wheels of the bench grinders and, therefore, is useful around the home, shop, or farm for all general grinding jobs such as sharpening kitchen cutlery, chisels, plane blades, knives, hatchets, axes, garden tools, and many other devices.

Another useful attachment that comes with home kits is finding many uses in jobs outside the home or home shop. This is the pull-apart extension handle which was originally designed to make the combo-tool with fabric pad or lamb's wool buff into a floor polisher. The aircraft industries and sheet-metal workers are finding this device very useful for light scrubbing and polishing of large surfaces that are hard to reach from a normal working position.

The drill chuck is, of course, a necessity for shop kits and will be found useful for many operations around the garage, home shop, factory, and general building work. This chuck was described in the chapter on portable drills and enables the combo-tool to be used with twist drills, paint mixer, small grinding bits, and other bit-type tools.

Specifications for the combination workshop. Although many of the accessory devices mentioned previously will work to a satisfactory degree with some ordinary electric drills, the power unit for such varied jobs should be one that is especially designed for different types of work. For working with all the various attachments that accompany a combination tool, the motor must be powerful and fast, mounted in a sturdy, die-cast aluminum alloy frame, and perfectly balanced for easy handling and smooth operation. You will notice in the picture that the handle is set low on the frame and that an extra handle attaches to the side of the motor housing. If you look back at the picture of the portable electric drills, you will notice that

the handle is set back at the rear of the case on the small
$\frac{1}{4}$-inch drills. This is true of all the lightweight electric drills,
including those in the inexpensive home and shop kits.

The drive of the combination tool should be a helical gear
arrangement, which doubles the power of similar tools of the
same size. The shaft should be larger and stronger than that
commonly found on small electric drills. The no-load speed of
the combination tool should be approximately 3000 rpm. The
switch should be an approved double-pole momentary trigger
located directly under the first finger position in the handle.
It should also have a lock button which can be quickly disen-
gaged by moving the trigger.

It is very important that other devices which are commonly
sold and advertised for use with the $\frac{1}{4}$-inch drill be carefully
considered as to design for efficiency and safety. No two different makes of drills are designed in the same way. Therefore, it follows that no device which is designed for one drill
will work equally well with others. Particular attention should
be given to the saws, grinders, belt sanders, and other special-
ties that are designed to imitate other portable power tools.
The speeds required for some of these operations are not always suited to electric drill or rotary drive. The devices used
to hold them and adapt the action to rotary motion are not
always substantial or of good, professional quality.

The additional tool attached to the hand drill often makes
a clumsy combination which is hard to control and difficult to
apply properly. This factor raises some questions as to the
safety of the operator as well as the work when these devices
are used. Another serious limitation to the quality and usefulness of these "gadgets" is the lack of adjustment for depth of
blade, angle cutting, belt tension, proper guards, and firm
attachment to the frame of the drive tool. Some of the sanders,
for instance, give a wide orbital motion of $\frac{1}{2}$ inch or more

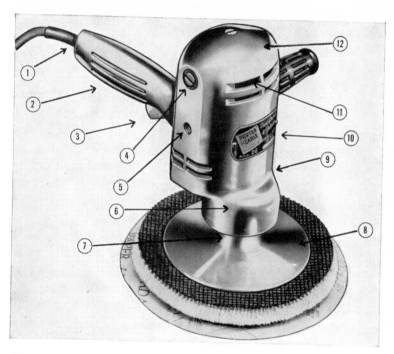

Fig. 27. Features of a good combo tool. (1) Cord enters machine at rear of handle and stays clear of work area. (2) Handle and motor housing built with good balance. (3) Switch is at finger tip for quick starting and stopping. (4) Motor brushes easily reached for inspection. (5) Alternate hole for inserting extra handle. (6) Helical gear drive for greater power and smoother operation. (7) Large shaft riding on precision ball bearings. (8) Pads and accessories fit close and fasten securely. (9) Case must be neatly formed and easy to keep clean. (10) Motor must be powerful for all kinds of jobs. (11) Wide vents provide for cool motor and access to commutator. (12) Over-all size must be compact for use in close work.

and set up a terrific vibration. This makes such a device very difficult to use in small areas and close quarters. Make sure the accessory is practical before you buy it for your combination workshop.

Using the combo-tool. It is not necessary to discuss all the operations for which the combination drill tools are practical. We shall give some attention to the more basic and more widely used applications. Others will naturally follow as the user acquires some experience with the tool and its accessories.

The abrasive disks are used for surfacing wood, metal, plastics, and other materials. Because of their greater power and special design for such work, the special combo-tool drive units are able to use a 6-inch-diameter sanding and grinding disk where ordinary hand drills are limited to the 5-inch disk. This increase in size allows 53 per cent more abrasive working area.

When starting to use the rotary sander, grasp the control handle firmly and move the tool freely without forced effort. The secret of all good sanding is a light touch with firm control of the machine. The guide handle can be changed to either side of the frame for right- or left-hand use. Use the machine with long, sweeping motions, back and forth, advancing over the surface to produce a smooth, continuous coverage. *For best results, tip the machine slightly forward with just enough pressure to bend the disk.* Do not hold the pad flat on the work so that the entire sanding surface is cutting. This will cause a very bad whirl stroke in the work and create considerable jumping in the tool. Using only one side causes the abrasive to operate largely in one direction and it also gives a smooth and light operation to the tool.

For all sanding on wood, use abrasive disks listed as grit S. For dry grinding on metal surfaces, use grit A. As a grinder for many jobs on larger parts and surfaces, the machine can be held in the hand and one should use only the fiber-abrasive

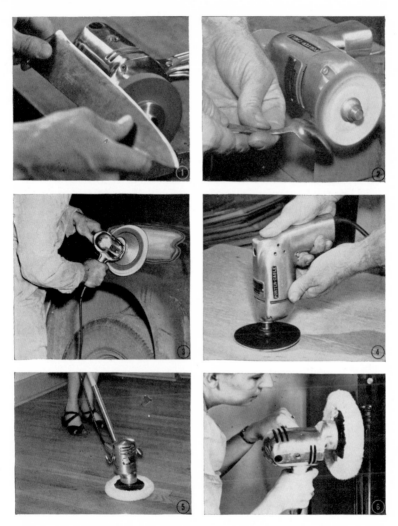

Fig. 28. The combo tool has many uses. (1) Sharpening cutlery and edged tools. (2) Polishing utensils and metal parts. (3) Sanding and finishing body work. (4) Disk sanding old or new surfaces. (5) Polishing floors with buffer head. (6) Buffing wax finish on furniture.

wheel that is especially designed for the combination drill. Small objects should be applied to the tool as it is firmly held in the bench stand. For wet grinding, use the disks listed as grit R. All of these disks are available in grades from $3\frac{1}{2}$ grit (very coarse) to 1/0 (very fine).

Polishing can be done with the lamb's wool buff, the pile fabric pad, or the cloth wheel buff. Be sure that the surface is properly prepared for waxing and polishing before the new wax coating is applied. Remove dirt and old wax with warm water, then mop dry. When fully dry, apply a thin coat of either liquid or paste wax with a soft cloth and allow to dry. Use the pile fabric pad to rub down the excess wax, then use the lamb's wool buff to give the finish a high gloss. The polisher is easier to handle if you tip it slightly to the right and allow the machine to "walk" itself back and forth across the work in wide, easy strokes. The buffs and pads can be cleaned quickly by using soap and water and letting them spin dry on the machine. It is a good idea to hold the machine in a paper bag or cardboard carton during the spin-dry operation.

Cleaning and polishing automobiles is a fast and efficient operation with the combo-tool. First of all, the car must be washed well and kept out of the sun. Use a liquid combination cleaner and polisher which contains no abrasive. Shake the liquid well and apply it with a soft cloth, rubbing gently and evenly over the entire surface. Start with the top and work down over the entire car. Let the liquid dry until it forms a white film. Attach the pile fabric pad direct to the rubber back-up pad and work down by floating the machine with just its own weight over the surface in long strokes. Do not try to remove all the cleaner with this pad. What is left in the corners and around the edges should be removed by hand or with the lamb's wool buff.

For the final operation, remove the pile fabric pad and slip the wool bonnet over the rubber back-up pad. Center the buff on the pad and pull the string up as tightly as possible, tucking in the loops so they will not fly out. Now go over the car carefully to bring the finish to a high luster. The big advantage of machine polishing is that not only is it faster than hand methods, but it does a better job of dirt and grime removal and gives a very high, brilliant luster. If the car should be very dirty, two operations as just described may be necessary.

Furniture and other objects around the house can be wax-polished in much the same way. It is important to remember that a thin coat of wax does a better job. It will polish easier and last longer. The polishing bonnets must be kept clean. For best results, use a wax that is especially prepared for machine finishing.

The wire brush is very practical when used with the more powerful combination-type drills for removing rust and hard-caked dirt from all parts of farm tools and shop equipment. Always apply objects to the wheel, or the wheel to the object, at a point below the center line of the wheel. Point any sharp edges down and outward from the surface of the wheel. *Do not turn sharp edges into the wire brush.* This precaution also applies to the abrasive wheels, grinding wheels, fabric pads, and buffers.

Drilling and boring operations with the combo-tool are exactly the same as described previously for the portable electric drill. Attach the three-jaw chuck directly to the spindle of the machine and use any of the straight shank drills or bits which are not over $\frac{1}{4}$ inch in diameter at the shank end. When drilling any metal with twist drills, it helps to add a few drops of oil to the tip of the drill bit. The oil will greatly increase the cutting action and reduce the possibility of burning the drill tip.

Care and maintenance of the combo-tool is much the same as that given for the $\frac{1}{4}$-inch drill in a previous chapter. Read and follow the instructions which come with the tool and be sure that you understand fully the purposes and uses of each of the accessories and attachments. By all means, follow the manufacturer's advice regarding grease and oil, maintenance tools, and when to call for repair service.

7 ═══ ROUTER-SHAPER-PLANER

The newest member of the portable tool family. The router, as a distinct form of portable machine tool, has been on the market for several years. In its early days, however, its use was confined to the furniture-making and cabinet shops and it was a rather expensive and cumbersome tool for the average person to use. Recently, however, this little-known tool has had the advantage of modern design and better motors and, as a result, is now available in a combination set which combines three basic tools of the router type each working from the same motor. This outfit furnishes woodworkers and shop craftsmen with much greater efficiency in electric power than these trades have ever enjoyed before.

The router is a tool for advanced carpentry and furniture making. In its modern efficiency, it can not only make the decorative edges on table tops and cut outlines for inlay jobs, but also do many ordinary and useful jobs around the house. For instance, a tool that can cut grooves and rabbets for cabinetwork, mortices for door hinges, fancy edges for bookcases and shelving, grooves for storm windows and weatherstripping, sink openings in counter tops, duplicate shapes of intricate design, circles and ovals with perfectly smooth edges, and corner rounding in all sorts of work can certainly earn its keep in anyone's shop. The router and its companions, the electric

99

plane and the shaper table, can do all those tricks and many more. It is little wonder that this new combination device has received such enthusiastic acclaim.

The operation of the router is unique in that it has no hand tool counterpart unless it be the carving chisel and mallet. Its principle of operation is quite different, however, being derived from and similar to that of the electric drill. The cutting bit is short and shaped for whatever task is desired, having three or four cutting edges of fairly small diameter. The shank of the bit is held in a small threaded chuck directly on the end of the shaft and the cutter is driven at a very high speed. The base of the machine is arranged so that the cutter can be guided over or along the work as the particular job demands. The depth of cut can be altered by raising or lowering the motor housing in the base frame. A variety of cutting bits enable the router to work a great many jobs on wood, plastics, composition materials, and the new pressed-wood materials. Carbide-tipped cutters are available for quantity work on abrasive and tough materials such as Formica and the denser plastics.

In learning to handle many of these new materials, shop workers and carpenters found that ordinary shop tools such as the bandsaw and table shaper just could not be adjusted to cut and shape such stuff effectively. The router was found to be the answer. The small, fast cutters will cut out irregular shapes and fancy edges smoothly and quickly without chipping or splitting the material. With the planer, which will also employ a variety of cutters, and the table shaper stand, this set of portable tools is just about the last word in professional shop efficiency for all woodworkers as well as the home craftsman and homeowner.

The router model shown here is the lightweight design built for the professional user as well as the home craftsman. A

Fig. 29. The plane-router kit and shaper attachment.

heavier model is available for heavy production work by large-scale contractors, sash and door plants, and millwork special-ists. The former tool will do all of the routing jobs that have been mentioned, but is not made for continuous, heavy-duty operation. The speed of the motor and the better quality of the light Universal motor make it a far superior tool to the old horsepower machines of the past.

One motor drives all these tools. The three parts to this shop combination are sold separately and with the motor, but the one motor will operate all these tools for the various jobs which each is designed to do. The motor case is interchangeable and slides quickly and accurately into the frame of each of these tools. If you should buy the router, for instance, the plane and the shaper are not considered accessories, but are addi-tional tools. There are many accessories that can be used with each one of the combinations. To the man in the trade who uses these tools almost daily and to the craftsman who needs professional quality equipment at a reasonable price, this port-able power setup is very hard to beat.

Features and specifications of the tools. The motor that drives the router-plane is usually a powerful 115 volt AC-DC, Universal which runs at the high speed of around 20,000 rpm. The motor case should be trim and slender and of highly polished die-cast aluminum alloy which is easy to keep clean. The switch must be a double-pole snap type which is recessed into the case at the rear of the housing where it is readily accessible. The shaft size is usually ⅝ inch at the chuck end and fitted with a large hex nut internally threaded. This large shaft arrangement allows a variety of adapters, arbors, and chucks to be quickly installed for various bits and cutters. The straight-shank bits are held in adapters of appropriate size and the screw-type cutters thread onto arbors. The motor shaft must have extra-heavy thrust bearings which will assure a long life of heavy work.

The router, which is pictured here with the motor attached, has a pair of spiral channels cut inside the base for supporting the motor and for facilitating finer adjustments. A large thumbscrew at the back draws the base tight to hold the motor exactly in position. With this arrangement, the depth of cut can be adjusted very closely and without setting the dial back to zero. The motor cannot slip during operation. Index marks around the upper edge of the base are on a sliding collar which can be moved to front or back for convenient reading. The depth of cut can be adjusted from $\frac{1}{64}$ to 1 inch quickly and accurately. Stock bits and cutters made for the router range from $\frac{1}{16}$ inch to $1\frac{3}{16}$ inch, and the shanks from $\frac{1}{16}$ inch to $\frac{1}{4}$ inch. It weighs only $5\frac{3}{4}$ pounds.

The power plane consists of the plane attachment which slips onto the case of the motor, an arbor for the spiral planing cutter, and the cutter blade. With a bench stand attachment, it can be quickly converted into a jointer. With shaper cutters, the plane serves very well as a portable molding plane. This feature is very handy for making grooves and channels for weatherstripping, inlay work, and molding edges. The maximum width of the cut with the plane cutter is $1\frac{13}{16}$ inches. The blade can be adjusted, while the machine is operating, from zero to $\frac{3}{32}$ inch. The apron assures perfect angle cutting, which is very difficult to accomplish with the ordinary hand plane. The apron can be adjusted for bevel cuts up to 25 degrees. The whole machine weighs 8 pounds.

While the work done by the shaper is quite similar to that of the router and planer, it is a different and a necessary tool for many jobs which are really difficult for the router or other tool. Moldings and beaded or rabbeted edges on curved or irregular shaped work can be done easily with the shaper head. A circular guide bracket permits smooth freehand shaping of carved pieces, strip molding, and ornamental woodwork. The working surfaces of the table are adjustable in depth from $3\frac{7}{8}$ inches to $3\frac{3}{16}$ inches. The width of the table is 12 inches. The maximum height of the cut is the same as the plane, $1\frac{13}{16}$ inches. The depth of cut can be adjusted, from zero to $\frac{3}{32}$ inch as a jointer and to $\frac{3}{4}$ inch as a shaper. The fence is adjustable to $\frac{3}{4}$ inch.

The shaper shown in the illustration consists of the main and adjustable fence assembly, the shaper table and bench stand, the circular guide bracket and posts, and the spindle assembly. The bench bracket serves as a support for the frame, and the base of the router is fastened to the underside of the table with a pair of clamps. The complete tool weighs just 12 pounds.

Accessory equipment for the router-shaper. If we consider the arbors, adapters, bushings, collars, spindles, and cutter shapes that are available for this set of tools in several sizes, we would have a list of several hundred items. Basically, however, we can list just a few of the more commonly used items that make up this part of the equipment and refer to the manufacturer's catalogs for the additional bits and cutters that may be needed for more specialized work.

The basic kit for the router includes an assortment which properly answers the question, "What bits should I start with?" The set has three frequently used cutters, two pilots, an arbor for all screw-type bits, and a 1-inch grinding wheel. The cutting bits are the $1\frac{3}{16}$-inch straight bit, the $\frac{3}{8}$-inch-radius beading bit, and the $\frac{3}{8}$-inch-radius cove bit. These are used for routing relief work; rabbet cuts for cabinet doors, drawers, mortises, etc.; routing for strip inlays; grooving for weatherstripping, tongue and groove joints; shaping decorative edges, corner rounding, drop-leaf table joints; fluting; channeling; dadoing; routing recessed designs; making contour cut-out patterns in signs; and a great many other applications. The principal types which may be included later are the dovetail bits, rabbeting bits, corner rounding, and the larger straight bits.

Other accessories are several devices which help considerably in doing special types of work. The most commonly used of these is the edge guide for making straight, even cuts; the corner chisel for making perfect, squared corners; and the plane cutter sharpening attachment. The latter, of course, is needed only with the plane. The corner chisel is a spring-action device that is used by placing it in the corner of the hinge mortise or other router cut and striking it with the hammer. The blade cuts the corner squarely and neatly and returns to its position by the pull of the spring.

For special uses of the router, the hinge-butt templet is especially useful. This tool is a unique device for automatically setting and routing the cuts necessary for placing door hinges. With this device, the router can cut hinge-butt mortises for fifteen doors per hour. To the general carpenter and house builder, this speed is a wonderful saving of time and money. The templet is automatically self-centering and adjustable to any door or jamb up to 8 feet high. It is self-measuring and error proof, making the hinges lie flush every time. The lock-face templet is a similar accessory for routing the slots for recessed door locks.

The occasional job of hinge mortising can be done very quickly and easily with the router without the use of the hinge-butt templet device. Mark the location of the hinge in the usual way and square the ends of the layout with the try

square. The back edge of the cut should come to about ¼ inch
of the back side of the door. Attach the edge guide to the base
of the router and adjust it so that the cutter will just reach the
back line when the guide is flush with the edge of the door.
Setting the edge of the cutter on one of the end lines, locate a
small block at the outer edge of the base to act as a guide and
square it with the try square. Now place the base of the
router on the door edge and lower the cutting bit until it just
touches the door. Set the depth measurement ring at zero on
the indicator mark of the motor housing. Tilt the machine and
advance the cutting bit to the thickness of the hinge. Starting
at the open side of the gain, cut along one edge until the edge
guide stops the movement. Move the router in and out, advancing along the gain until the stop at the other side is
reached. By using one of the straight bits about ¾ inch in
diameter, you can obtain a clean and uniform mortise very
easily. The radius that is left in the corners can be squared
with the chisel and mallet. (See figure 33.)

How to use the cutting bits in the basic kit. The illustration showing the profile of the cutting bits and the cuts they
make will clearly reveal the wide variety and nature of the
work the router will do. The bits in this basic kit show all of
the principal uses of the router-shaper combination and the
methods employed in such work. In the description of each of
these bits, some typical operations will be pictured so that you
can get a good idea of the many ways in which the router can
be used.

ARBOR, ADAPTERS, AND PILOTS. Only one arbor is necessary and it is a simple shaft of ¼-inch diameter having a
threaded end for holding the screw-type bits. The various bits
will thread directly onto the end of the arbor and the shank is
inserted into the chuck of the machine. Two wrenches work-

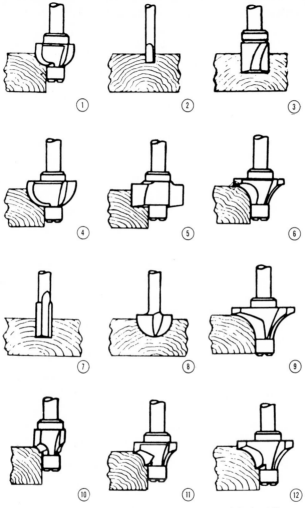

Fig. 30. Types of router-shaper cutters. (1) Small cove bit. (2) Straight bit. (3) Grooving bit. (4) Large cove bit. (5) Rabbeting bit. (6) Small beader. (7) Straight bit. (8) Core box bit. (9) Corner rounding. (10) Small bead. (11) Medium bead. (12) Large bead.

ing opposite forces tighten the chuck onto the hex-sided end of the machine shaft. Only finger tightness should be used in threading the bit onto the arbor. The pilots, of which there are two sizes in the set, thread into a hole at the end of the cutting bit to provide a bearing surface with which to guide the tool against the edge of the work. These small, round buttons regulate the lateral depth. It should be pointed out here that the edge against which the pilot acts as a guide must be smooth and formed exactly to the required shape of the cut. Any bumps, waves, or other imperfections will be duplicated in the cut as the pilot guides along the edge. The pilots can also be used to vary the size and pattern of cuts made with the cove, beading, and corner-rounding bits. The adapters, none of which are included in the basic kit, are sleeves of various hole sizes having an outside diameter of $\frac{1}{4}$ inch. Their purpose is merely to adapt smaller shanks to the required $\frac{1}{4}$-inch diameter to fit the chuck. They are slotted along the side so that when the chuck nut is turned up tight, the smaller shank is gripped securely to the shaft.

STRAIGHT BITS. The straight bit included in the basic kit is a one-piece cutter with a $\frac{1}{4}$-inch shank and $\frac{1}{4}$-inch-diameter cutting end. Similar bits are available up to $\frac{1}{2}$-inch cutting diameter. These bits are used for routing out the background of carvings, panel work, cutting rabbets, and making strip inlays. In general, the average cut should not exceed $\frac{1}{4}$ inch in depth; although, in soft wood, deeper cuts can be taken if the bit is sharp and the tool is fed slowly into the wood. The usual practice, when deep rabbets or inlay cuts are to be made, is to make two or more passes, each taking out about $\frac{1}{4}$ inch of material. It is necessary to take smaller bites when rabbeting or grooving hardwoods than when working softwoods.

The straight bits, in sizes from $\frac{5}{8}$-inch diameter to $1\frac{3}{16}$

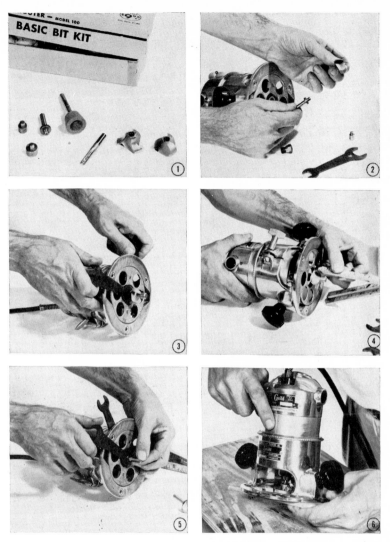

Fig. 31. Setting up the router. (1) Seven parts of the basic kit do many jobs. (2) Cove bit screws onto the arbor. (3) Arbor is tightened into the chuck. (4) Measure depth of cutter adjustment. (5) Straight bit fits directly into the chuck. (6) Check zero setting of blade tip with strip of wood.

inch, are also made as a screw-type cutter for attaching to the
arbor. This type of cutter is excellent for rabbeting and dado
work. These straight cutters may be said to be the backbone
of the router business. They will do the greatest variety of
work and can be adapted to more different operations than any
other bits. For straight-line cutting of face edges, rabbets,
dadoes, and grooves, the edge guide which fastens directly to
the base of the machine is used to keep the line of the cut
straight and parallel to the edge. Naturally, the edge on which
the guide moves must be straight and smooth.

Relief work and recessed designs may be cut with the router
guided solely by hand. One needs to be somewhat of an artist,
however, to follow a design freehand; and, when the cutting
action of the bit is partially concealed by the router base, this
becomes a rather tight job. Remove the subbase. Template
guides, therefore, make much more accurate work possible and
are absolutely necessary when duplicate pieces are to be made.
This is one field of woodworking where the router stands su-
preme and alone. Such jobs can not be done with any other
tool. Furthermore, the cutting of circles and curved shapes, if
done with a pattern, is much easier to do with the router than
with the band saw. Such cuts with the router need no further
smoothing or edging.

THE BEADING BIT. The beading bit included in the basic
kit is the ⅜-inch-radius screw type which is attached to the
arbor. Any one of the pilots can be used in the small end of
the bit for guiding the cut and altering its size. If the full
radius of the bit is wanted, the smallest pilot is used. If a
smaller depth of cut is needed, the larger pilot is used. The
larger pilot eliminates the bottom bead on the cutter and is
commonly used for corner rounding. The beading bits are
used on picture frames, molding, edges of furniture, and table
tops. The one in the basic kit also makes the drop-leaf table

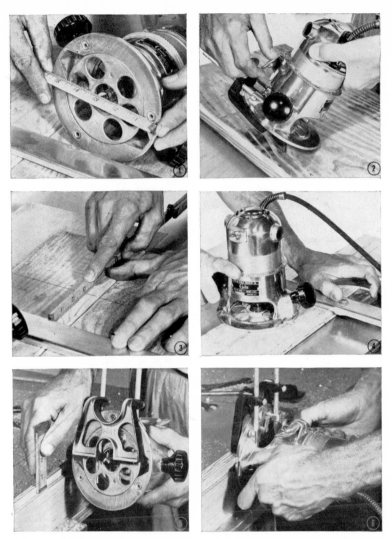

Fig. 32. Dadoes and rabbets with the router. (1) Measure the edge
of the bit from the rim of the base. (2) Tighten the depth adjustment after advancing the bit. (3) Move the guide edge exact distance from line of cut. (4) Hold guide firmly and move router across
the work. (5) Check each cut before advancing the cutter. (6) Use
the edge guide for straight, exact grooves.

cut for the table side of the joint. When making any of these cuts, always use a piece of scrap first to make a trial cut.

THE COVE BIT. The opposite side of the drop-leaf table joint is made with the cove bit. This cutter attaches in the same manner as the beading bit and the same pilot and machine adjustments on the machine must be used for matching edges. The cove bit included in the set is the same radius as the beader. The cove bits are also used for all concave cuts in molding, picture frames, panel rails, cabinets, bookcases, and table tops.

THE GRINDING WHEEL. The last item in the basic kit is also a very useful one and essential to the proper use of all the other cutters. The grinding wheel is a small cup wheel with a $\frac{1}{4}$-inch shank which fits directly into the chuck of the router. While it may be used for removing burrs and for small grinding operations on metal parts, its chief use is that of keeping the cutting bits sharp and in first-class condition. Remove the motor from the router frame and insert the grinding wheel shank, tightening it securely with the wrenches. Hold the motor housing in one hand and against the body so that the machine can be held steady. The cutter to be sharpened is held in the other hand and the two are brought together as necessary to obtain a sharp and even cutting edge. *Grind lightly and only on the inside of the cutting edge.* Touch up the ends of the bits when they need it and always grind the clearance angle the same as that on the original bit.

Shop hints and tricks of the trade. Here are several ways that the router is used in the shop. These will help suggest others to the user. All of the methods illustrated are simple to carry out and require no additional accessories other than scraps and wood patterns which can be made right on the job. A templet guide tip is a useful device to have and is very inexpensive. These guides are made in several sizes to accommo-

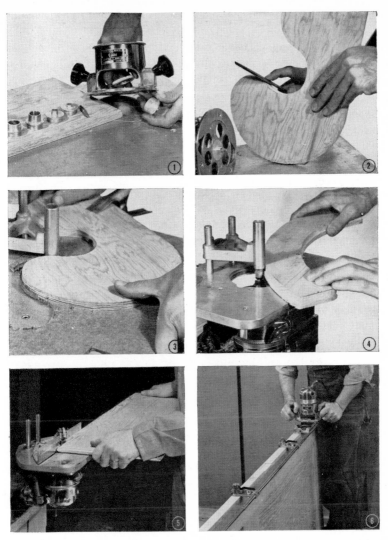

Fig. 33. Using the templet guides on router and shaper. (1) The different sized guides fasten to the base with a retainer ring. (2) Templets must have smooth and even edges. (3) Templet rides against the guidepost on shaper table. (4) Curved edges and shapes can be handled at almost any angle. (5) Shaper guide fence set up for rabbeting cabinet doors. (6) Templet guides are used with the butt-hinge mortising jig.

date the different sizes of cutters. The templet guide, or bit guide tip, is a short cylinder or sleeve which fits into the cutter opening on the router subbase and which locks with a large lock nut on the inside of the base. The nose of the guide shields the templet from the cutter and furnishes a rigid bearing surface for guiding the bit. Again, the edges of the templet or pattern on which this guide will move must be accurate and smooth. Any defects in the pattern will be transferred to the cutter.

Another important precaution is that of fastening the work securely in a vise or to the table. Clamps and scrap wood supports may be arranged as necessary to hold the work in place and to provide clearance for the cutter. When working around corners you will also find that less trouble is encountered if the cut is started on a cross-grain edge and finished on the parallel grain. This procedure will avoid splintering the corner at the end of the cut. The direction of the cutting operation should always be such that the router is pulled against the material or the guiding surface and not away from it. When using a guiding surface or templet edge, the movement must always ride steadily against the guide. Any deviation will make an uneven cut.

CUTTING CIRCLES AND OVALS. A very simple method of cutting a circle in plywood or any other material for which you have a suitable bit is by use of a nail or screw and a piece of wire. Work from the underside of the material to avoid marring the surface with a nail hole. Find the center and the radius of the circle you want to cut and put a nail or wood screw at the exact center. It should not go through the material, but must hold securely against the pull of the machine. Put a straight-edged cutter in the router and set the machine on the material so that the bit is directly on the outside of the circumference mark. Now take a piece of soft, strong wire

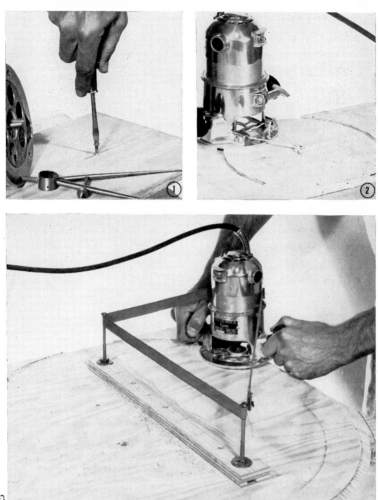

Fig. 34. Cutting curves and circles with the router. (1) Locate a firm support at the exact center of the arc. (2) Swing the router on a wire around the screw center. (3) Two centers are necessary for an oval shape.

and make a loop which will go around the base of the router, above the handles, and around the screw or nail in the center. Take up on the wire carefully until the wire is taut and the machine is exactly in position to cut on the line. Raise the router and advance the cutting bit about $\frac{1}{4}$ inch. Hold the machine taut against the wire and start the motor. Lower the bit into the work and start the movement in a counterclockwise direction, keeping the machine taut against the wire loop. Keep the tool moving or the blade will heat up and cause a burn on the wood and damage the bit. Do not feed too fast, but move rapidly enough to keep the tool bit cutting. You will not be able to go all the way around because of the clamps. Go as far as you can, lift the bit out of the cut before stopping the machine, move the clamps and continue to complete the circle. If a bevel, cove, or beaded edge is wanted on the finish side, turn the disk over, put the other cutter in and use the pilot in the end of the bit as a guide.

Rounded ends and corners can be made in the same manner by working the router around the semicircle or quarter circle to a point where the sides of the layout become tangent to the circumference. Ovals are made in much the same way except that two center points must be located and the wire placed around the three objects: screws in the two centers and the router base. The router can move cleanly around the full oval with the pull against the screw or nail centers holding it in the required radius. These operations are shown in the pictures.

RELIEF CUTS AND RECESSED DESIGNS. The irregular curves and edges necessary for design work can best be made with a templet guide tip on the tool and a guide or templet cut from $\frac{1}{2}$-inch plywood. One edge of this guide tool should be very straight and smooth for cutting the straight-line sections. The other sides should have various curves somewhat like the draftsman's curve and with arcs that correspond to the size of those in the design. This templet can be moved around as necessary to follow the pattern of the picture or layout. Use the templet guide tip on the base of the router and the bit will not cut to the edge of the templet or guiding piece. The outside surface of the tip rides against the guide and the cutting bit is even smaller than the inside diameter of the tip. Try the cut on a scrap piece and measure the exact distance that the guide will have to lie behind the line of the cut. If duplicate letters or designs are to be made, either relief or cut out, much time will be saved and accuracy gained by cutting a stencil from plywood. The openings will have to allow for the size of the templet guide tip, but the cutting can be routed out in a hurry once the pattern is made. This technique is useful for camp signs, name plates, mail box markers, and inlay work. For large relief areas in such pieces, cut a slot opening in the templet work guide and move it across the area as the work advances.

REPEATED AND IRREGULAR SHAPES. Decorative edges on woodwork are often needed for porches, house trim, cabinet tops, shelving, and display pieces. Such designs should be cut out of plywood for a pattern, smoothed, and made perfect for guiding the router. You will need only one sequence of the design up to the point where it is to be repeated. When used, the pattern is moved along the material as the cutting advances. Again, allowance will have to be made for the extra diameter of the templet guide tip and all sharp corners and narrow openings in the design will have to be within reach and capacity of the cutting bits.

Another convenient shape for a permanent templet is an *L,* or angle, cut out of plywood and similar to the carpenter's square. The legs should be 14 inches on one inside edge and 8 on the other. The width of both legs should be the same, about 4 inches. If both the inside and the outside angles are carefully made and smoothed to a true 90 degrees, the angle can be used every time the routing job calls for such a square angle. When you are cutting a rectangular opening, the angle templet can be fixed on one corner with the clamps, two sides routed, then moved to the opposite corner and the remaining sides cut.

CABINET AND FURNITURE JOINTS. In the chapter on the use of the portable saw (chapter 4), an explanation was given for the cutting of dadoes, rabbets, grooves, gains, lap joints, and the tenon side of the mortise and tenon joint. All of these cuts may be made with the router and in a similar manner, using the edge guide where the cut runs parallel and near the edge of the material (within reach of the edge guide). Where the cut runs across the width of the material, any type of square guide may be used to guide the router. The same cross-cut square that was made for the saw will work very well. It is placed back from the line of the cut just far enough so that the edge of the router base can move against it and the bit left cutting on the line as desired.

Looking again at the illustration of common wood joints in chapter 10, you will now recognize several operations that can be done readily with the router and you will also see a possibility for making the dovetail joints—work which could not be done with the saw. The tongue and groove joints are a very simple job for the shaper table and the straight-face cutters arranged on the shaper spindle. This operation is clearly illustrated in the photograph. The mortise side of the mortise-tenon joints can be cut with the router using straight bits, a templet guide tip, and a cut-out templet clamped securely to the material being cut. The depth of the cut is limited to $1\frac{1}{4}$ inches, but this is sufficient for most cabinet and furniture mortises. The through mortise and the open mortise can be completed in thicker pieces by transferring the layout accu-

Fig. 35. Tongue and groove joint on the shaper table. (1) Set the cutter to remove one-third for the groove. (2) Select a spacer ring that fits the groove. (3) Use two cutters with the spacer to make the tongue. (4) Close-up showing cutter exactly to the edge. (5) Same arrangement can be used with the plane. (6) The tongue and groove joint for close-fitting edges.

rately to the opposite side. This will give a total through cut of 2½ inches.

Dovetailing is the most secure and advanced type of joint to use for drawers, cabinet corners, and boxes where good construction is required. It is also the most difficult joint to make. The layout is actually the most difficult part, for both sides have to be measured and marked very accurately so that, when cut, the opposing socket and pin will fit closely. The tapered sides of both the socket and pin should lie about 70 or 80 degrees to the parallel ends. Sharper angles create the danger of splitting when the parts are put together. To locate the lines of the dovetail joint, use the thickness of each of the sides to measure off on the other. This lays off the shoulder line and the depth of cut on each piece. The pins are usually cut out first and then used to mark off the lines of the sockets. Cutting these out is a tedious and painstaking job when using the backsaw, chisel, and mallet.

By using the dovetail bit and a quickly made slotted guide, any of the dovetail joints can be made very quickly and very neatly with the router. The illustration shows the setup and cutting of the half-blind, or lap, dovetail which is the most commonly used of the dovetail joints and the one that is always necessary for joining drawer fronts to the sides. The first step is that of making the slotted templet. Use Masonite (tempered) or a piece of ¼-inch plywood and cut a straight and smooth edge about 12 inches long. Using a very sharp pencil or pointed scriber and a clearly marked rule, mark off the slots exactly ¼ inch in width and ½ inch apart. Using the try square, draw lines through these marks to a depth line 2 inches back from the straightedge. Start this slotted guide in a fairly long piece of material so that you will have room to move the squaring guide down along the edge to reach all the slots.

Now place the pattern material on a piece of soft scrap-

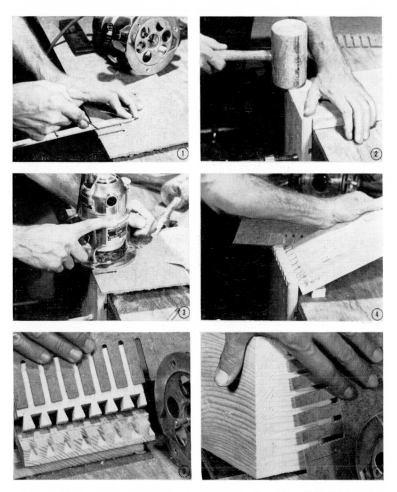

Fig. 36. Dovetail corners with the router and guide. (1) Make the guide with accurate spacing for the fingers. (2) Clamp the front and sides of drawer to the workbench. (3) With finger guide clamped down, run the router in slots. (4) Pick up the front and lift straight over to fit parts. (5) Close-up of the two parts and the slotted guide. (6) The finished joint, showing a neat and tight fit.

wood, line up the edges to the front, and place both pieces flat on the table. Clamp the ends securely so that neither piece can move. Using the straight bit of $\frac{1}{4}$-inch diameter in the router and a try square as a guide, rout out the $\frac{1}{4}$-inch slots which you have marked. Sight every one of these slots carefully and make this piece perfectly because this accuracy will determine the neatness and accuracy of all the dovetail joints you make with it. Cut each slot back to the 2-inch line. With fine sandpaper, smooth the edges of each slot so that there are no tiny splinters to balk or deflect the cutter.

The reason for the $\frac{1}{4}$-inch slots placed $\frac{1}{2}$-inch apart is the size of the dovetail bit. The shank of the bit, which is to be guided into the slots, is $\frac{1}{4}$ inch in diameter. The end of the dovetail bit is $\frac{1}{2}$ inch in diameter. Thus, the bottoms of the sockets will be exactly the same width as the ends of the pins. The reason for the 2-inch length of the slots is to provide an entering guide for the cutting bit to enter the wood without deflecting.

When you have made a true and square finger guide, the job of cutting dovetail joints is done for all time. Now all you have to do is to lay the drawer front face down on the worktable with the end squared at the edge of the table. Clamp it in place. Clamp the drawer side piece to the side of the table so that the end is exactly flush with the inner side of the drawer front. Before fastening the clamp, move the drawer side to the left so that its right edge (the bottom edge) is exactly $\frac{1}{4}$ inch to the left of the lower edge of the drawer front.

With both pieces securely clamped down and squared with each other, place the slotted guide in position on the drawer front so that the first slot to the right clears the edge of the vertical, or drawer side, piece. Locate the back ends of the slots exactly parallel to the outer edge of the side piece and back just twice the thickness of the side piece. This will allow some half-inch or more of the fingers to project forward of the setup. Now place the dovetail cutter in the router and advance the bit for its full cutting length plus the thickness of the guide templet. Make sure the templet is clamped in position and the router can then be worked quickly in and out of all the slots. After the cuts are made, release the clamps and pick up the drawer front, lifting it directly over and toward you so that the sockets are facing down. Line up the bottom edges and the parts will slide easily and firmly together for a perfect fit. Practice this a couple of times with scrap material and, if necessary, rework the finger guide until the joints fit perfectly. It is better to have them tight so that they have to be forced together with the mallet than it is to leave them free and easily moved. Tight dovetails will make a tight, secure drawer joint.

THE BIG SECRET OF ROUTER WORK. Enough has been said here and pictured in the photographs to convince anyone that the secret of sure and repeated success with the router lies in the making and using of accurate guides and templets. With some experience, quite a bit of router work can be done with the machine guided solely by the hands. The speed at which the motor runs makes the tool very easy to guide and hold in place. This is particularly true if the cutters are kept very sharp, as they should be at all times. This same speed and sharpness, however, will take a nasty bite out of the material if the bit or machine should be accidentally deflected or pulled aside from its proper path. Be sure that the base of the machine rests firmly on the work, a securely fastened templet or other guide arrangement. It will not make a square cut if the machine is tilted.

Care and maintenance of the router-shaper-plane. Since the one motor drives all these tools, care and maintenance problems are at a minimum. Keep the motor clean of dust by blowing out the air passages frequently. Do not allow dust to

collect inside the motor housing. Be sure that the current is
115 volts and that the extension or lead wire is Number 14 or
larger. Make sure that the ground wire is connected to a positive ground. The other parts of the combination kit require
the same common-sense care and attention that all good tools
require. Keep the parts clean and the adjustments working
properly. It seems almost unnecessary to mention the necessity for selecting the proper collets or adapters to fit the various bits. Be sure the one selected is the right size and that the
cutting bit is securely tightened before starting the motor.
Again, keep it sharp!

Lubrication is usually not necessary on these tools. The
precision ball bearings in the motor are grease sealed for the
life of the bearings.

How to sharpen the plane cutter. The plane cutter sharpening attachment is so simple to operate that anyone can
sharpen the blade and be back on the job in three minutes.
This attachment is one that will certainly pay for itself in
money and time saved by keeping your own cutters sharp.
Remove the motor from the case of the plane and take the
cutter off the spindle. Replace the cutter with the aluminum sleeve and the small, cup grinding wheel which comes with
the kit. Slip the cutter onto the shaft of the grinding attachment and fit the motor into the opening provided at the side
of the frame. Make sure that the grinding wheel is not qu'te
touching the cutter.

Slide the pin on the collar of the grinding shaft into one of
the spiral grooves in the long bronze bushing and move the
cutter past the grinding wheel, turning the knurled adjustment
screw at the front of the fixture until the cutter is very close,
but not touching, the stone. Now, make sure that the motor
switch is in the "off" position and plug the cord into the outlet.
Push the cutter back and forth past the grinding wheel, at the

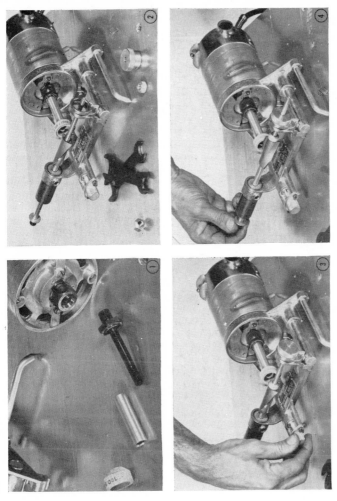

Fig. 37. Sharpening the plane blade. (1) These three parts assemble on the router motor. (2) The cutter grinder assembly holds both blade and motor. (3) Adjustment screw advances the blade toward the stone. (4) Slide bar moves blade across face of stone in even stroke.

same time turning the adjusting screw to advance the feed of the cutter. When the wheel touches, draw the cutter all the way back, make a slight, advancing turn of the adjustment screw, start the motor, and pass the cutter all the way across the stone. Now withdraw the slide and make a half turn to the opposite slot and advance the other cutting edge across the stone. Be sure to make a full pass with each blade after each adjustment of the knurled feed screw. When sharpening the plane cutter, as when sharpening any cutting edge, remove as little material as possible and always stone just a slight bit at a time. In this way, the edge will be both even and sharp and the cutting edge will last longer. The cutter can now be put back on the plane.

8 ═ OTHER PORTABLE TOOLS

The choice is wide, the tools are many. Now that we have jumped the psychological, mechanical, and economic barriers in the making and using of portable electric tools, the limits of their application seem boundless. By the time a book can be written and published on the subject of portable tools, there will be other new ones which have not been covered. This book is not intended, therefore, to be an absolutely final word on the subject, but is aimed at an explanation and illustration of those practical tools that are available today and that have been found to have the widest application in everyday usage. The principles of these tools are basic, however, and an understanding of their workings and characteristics will enable one to judge and use other and newer tools.

Many of the portable tools that could come under the heading of this chapter are merely additional applications of tools that have already been explained and need no further details. The flexible shaft, for instance, is a further extension of the electric hand drill. The motor is usually larger and faster, the shaft revolving in a special flexible casing, and the business end working with an ordinary drill chuck or any of the alternate heads described for the combination drill-sander-buffer. The small grinder, which has been so popular for so many years for the handicraft trades and novelty workers, is a small and somewhat faster electr'c drill. We do not mean to ignore them nor to belittle them by not including a detailed account of their structure and use. They are very useful and efficient tools, but are somewhat beyond the scope and intent of this book.

There is another group of tools that operate by the force of compressed air. These include paint sprayers, wrenches, drills, hammers, sanders, and even saws, but their general use and application follow very closely the pattern that we have covered with the portable, electric-power tools. Included in this chapter are those special-purpose electric tools that are found to be the most practical and generally useful to the largest number of workmen in various fields.

Bench grinders. While these very necessary shop tools are not properly portable, they are considered of such importance to the maintenance of all tools that some word about them is included. Here is one place where, again, the buyer must be cautioned about price. A good bench grinder costs money and one must be careful in buying the cut-rate "bargains" which are often found for sale in advertising flyers. A good bench grinder must, above all, be heavy enough to work efficiently and accurately without vibration. It must also be adequate for the tasks it is put to and it must be safe in operation.

A good bench grinder has four features. First, there is a sturdy base which can be bolted securely to the bench. Second, there is a smooth and completely enclosed case around the motor and all moving parts. Third, there is a complete shield around the wheel to protect the worker from flying bits and serious damage in case the wheel should break. Fourth, there is a sturdy and adjustable tool rest, or work rest, for steadying the work as it is applied to the wheel.

Specifications of these grinders are about the same, but the horsepower increases with the wheel size. The 6-inch wheel is on a model with $\frac{1}{4}$-horsepower rating, the 10-inch wheel is on a model rated at 1 horsepower. The weight of these bench grinders illustrates clearly what we mean by substantial support. The smallest weighs 43 pounds, the largest, 168. In wheel speed, no load, the 6-inch, 7-inch, and 8-inch grinders are rated at 3450 rpm, but the large 10-inch wheel is only 1750 rpm.

Uses of bench grinders are limited, as are all tools, by the size and working characteristics of the particular model. The small, 6-inch wheel is ideal for small shops, garages, home workshops, farms, and manufacturing plants where only intermittent use is necessary. The $\frac{1}{3}$ horsepower, 7-inch model is designed for larger shops, school and industrial woodworking shops, automotive and body shops for general grinding tasks. The $\frac{1}{2}$-horsepower, 8-inch model is used where metal working and more heavy-duty grinding is encountered. The large, 10-inch unit is the industrial, welding shop, foundry, and machine-shop tool which is designed for heavy-duty, continuous operations. It is powered to handle all heavy duty grinding jobs. On all models there is one fine wheel and one coarse wheel, either of which can be quickly changed for special and varied work.

Before mounting a grinding wheel, tap it to be sure it is not cracked. A ringing sound indicates a sound wheel; a dull thud, a cracked wheel. When the motor is started and the wheel is revving up, stand clear until it reaches its full speed and is running normally. Always wear goggles or keep the glass guard or plastic shield in place. Do not use the side of the wheel if the face will do the work. If you must use the side, do not exert too great pressure.

Hedgeshear. A great many people of a great many trades have spent countless back-breaking hours trimming hedges, shrubbery, tall grass, and weeds. Usually, and except for professional caretakers and gardeners, this work is not done for wages, but on the home property. Now, the principle of portable electric power has been applied to this irksome task and the labor of a day's work can now be done in less than an hour. The hedgeshear illustrated here is a tool of professional quality, yet is so constructed that anyone can learn to operate it with skill in a few minutes. Whatever the requirements of the trimming job, whether a park, estate, or the little plot of shrubbery at home, this tool is both simple to use and inexpensive to own.

The hedgeshear is designed for one-hand operation. It can

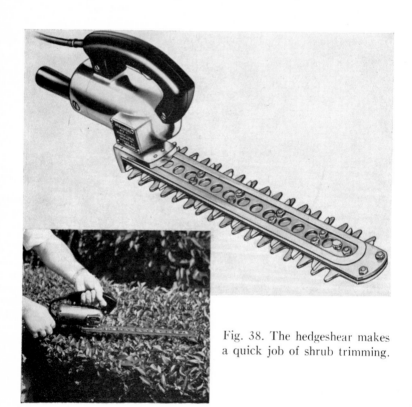

Fig. 38. The hedgeshear makes a quick job of shrub trimming.

be used flat or at any angle and without tiring because the machine and motor are perfectly balanced to operate without vibration. The switch is held in one hand and the tool in the other. In that way, the operator has perfect control of the cutting action. The blades are self-honing and, outside of occasional oiling, the machine needs no more than usual and reasonable care.

SUGGESTIONS FOR USING THE HEDGESHEAR. When hooking up the electric hedgeshear, use No. 14 gage wire for the extension. It will operate efficiently on extension lengths up to 500 feet. An extension handle of strong, lightweight aluminum permits trimming tall decorative bushes and hedges as well as trellis growths and light pruning on young trees. On the tops of hedges, incline the cutter bar slightly in the direction in which you are cutting. Use a sweeping motion and rake the cut twigs from the hedge as you go along. On the sides of the hedge, cut from the ground up and keep the cutter bar parallel with the ground and slightly turned into the hedge.

The hedgeshear can be used for light pruning or shaping. In this operation a slight sawing motion is helpful. This action keeps the branches dropping into the slots rather than being held on the end of the bar. With a few minutes practice, the tool can be used for many trimming jobs. Be careful, however, not to catch wire or steel cable in the teeth. The tool will not jam on wood, but metal may nick or bend the teeth. As far as care is concerned, the tool needs little attention. Use a brush and fresh water, if necessary, and wipe the metal parts clean after using. Oil the cutter bar with any good grade of medium oil before starting to trim. Apply oil freely to the oil cup at the end of the bar and keep the teeth and chain well lubricated. Keep just enough of the special grease for the worm gear to coat the gear while it is running. Inspect the gear chamber every month, but do not use too much grease.

Electric chain saw. Somewhat related to the hedgeshear but a much larger and more powerful tool is the electric chain saw which has recently been put on the market. This tool is one of great value to farmers, builders, homeowners, tree surgeons, and many others who frequently have to cut timber or trees. It is ideal for clearing wooded lots, cutting cord and pulpwood, limbing, topping, felling trees, notching larger trees, and cutting large timbers in wrecking and building work. It can cut any timber from a sapling to a tree 28 inches in diameter. It is a lightweight, one-man saw, and can be used in many places where a heavier tool would be unmanageable.

The chipper chain runs at 1400 feet per minute and makes a smooth, clean cut on all hard and soft woods. The sharp, log-gripping teeth are hard chromed and rust resistant. The teeth are set to both sides of the blade, which eliminates the tendency for the saw to pull away from the user or walk out of the cut. The 10-amp. motor provides power for even the toughest jobs. One big advantage of the electric power saw is the easy starting feature. Even in the coldest weather, it starts at once and runs when it is needed.

CUTTING WITH THE CHAIN SAW. When using the saw at some distance from the power source, use a heavy wire extension. A No. 14 gage wire is recommended up to 100 feet, No. 12 up to 150 feet, and No. 10 up to 250 feet. In cases where the saw is needed beyond the reach of an electric outlet, a 1500-watt generator is available. This efficient power source is described in this chapter.

The electric chain saw is light enough and so perfectly balanced that it can be used in any position. It weighs only 18 pounds and, once started, cuts its own way into the wood. The log-traction teeth at the base of the blade help considerably and should always be used on felling and top bucking operations. Good lubrication of the chain is very important to the

Fig. 39. Using the chain saw. (1) When felling a tree, cut out branches first. (2) Cut a deep notch in direction of fall. (3) Cut trunk at back and just above lower side of notch. (4) Limbs can be cut quickly into shorter lengths. (5) Push rocker teeth against log and lift handle of saw. (6) Keep light oil handy and lubricate teeth after each cut.

performance of the machine. Use the special cutter bar oil after every cut.

It is very important in felling a tree to make a notch on the side toward which the tree is to fall. The depth of the notch should be about one-third the diameter of the tree. After completing the notch, cut from the opposite side and about one inch above the horizontal cut. This method will prevent the butt of the tree from thrusting backward as the trunk is cut through. When bucking, keep the motor end low and chuck the log traction teeth into the back of the log. The teeth will form a pivot upon which the rear handle can be raised to force the cutting chain into the log.

The chain is the most important part of the saw. It should be inspected daily for sharpness and damage. It takes only a few minutes to restore a keen cutting edge to dulled teeth and it will be minutes well spent. Care and repair of the saw and the chain are fully described in the folder which comes with the tool.

Portable electric power plant. Now that portable electric tools have become a permanent necessity to a great many trades and handicrafts, the development of the final step toward complete portability was inevitable. A lightweight gasoline-driven generator now provides an independent source of electric power beyond the limits of wall outlets and power lines. This little generator is made in two models and both will provide enough electric power to run any of the electric tools that we have described. Particularly to builders and construction people and even to farmers, woodsmen, road maintenance crews, and to telephone linemen, these little power houses have been a welcome addition to the portable toolbox. Curiously enough, even power company linemen and construction crews have found these generators handy to have around when storms damage the power lines and black out the usual source of electricity.

The smaller model electric power generator is a 1500-watt direct current unit supplying 115 volts at 13 amps. It has a 3 hp single-cylinder engine and four electric outlets. Weighing only 75 pounds, it can be carried by one man and is compact enough to be carried in the luggage trunk of the car. The DC current is powerful enough for all electric tools having a 115 volt AC-DC motor. The larger generator weighs 135 pounds and provides alternating current. It has a two-man carrying handle.

These portable generators have many other uses than just the operation of electric power tools. They may be used as a mobile power source for floodlight units for construction, public events, emergency crews, police and fire departments, and general farm use. As a stand-by emergency power plant, these units are excellent for all places where a constant current is a vital necessity. Temporary camps and unwired cottages can use the generators for light, refrigeration, radio, pumps, washing machines, and other ultilities as well as for electric tools.

9 ≡ SAFETY
AND TOOL MAINTENANCE

Is the tool safe to use? The first question that should always be present in the mind of the safe workman is the one stated at the beginning of this paragraph. The answer always has two parts: it must be the right tool for the job and the tool must be in suitable working condition. Errors in using the wrong tool are most often found in the common hand-tool department; but, since many hand tools are used on or with power tools, the question is one of importance to the power-tool worker. The wrench must always be the right size for the nut. Never use pliers instead of a wrench. Never use a wrench as a hammer. Never use a screwdriver as a pry bar. The "nevers" and "don'ts" are legion and the good workman doesn't have to worry about them. He knows what tools are made to do and he knows how to use them.

Electric tools are designed for specific jobs. Use the right saw blades, bits, and drills. Make sure the blades and drills are always sharp. Check the adjustments of the saw to make sure they are clear of obstructions and work freely. If the tool has been dropped, check it carefully for damage and have the damage repaired before you attempt to use the tool. In the case of drills, inspect the drill bits as well as the drill itself.

Make a habit of inspecting and cleaning and oiling all your power tools at regular intervals. Keep sufficient grease in the gear boxes. Keep the air holes clear. Inspect the blade guards and switches to make sure they are working safely. This is one field where frequent inspection and care pays big dividends.

Safety with electricity. It is often true that in using an electric tool, we are merely substituting one mechanical hazard for another. The electric tool operates so much faster than hand-operated tools that the hazard is multiplied many times, both in possibility of harm and the extent of damage. These problems should be understood by the workman before he uses portable electric tools. If he understands the tool he is using and knows how to keep it in good condition, these hazards will be largely eliminated. The principal danger in using electric tools, however, is from electric shock. Flash burns, falls caused by reaction from minor shocks, and severe shocks causing physical damage are the principal types of electric accidents.

All electric powered tools should be grounded with a good ground connection. The portable tools described in this book are equipped with a third wire in the cord which is grounded to the case of the tool. The post or clip at the end of the wire should always be connected to a water pipe, an electric conduit, or a piece of pipe or metal rod driven into the ground. By all means, don't depend on the outlet or cable casing being properly grounded until you have examined it yourself. In wet weather, damp areas, or when the worker is wet with perspiration, the danger from such electric shock is much greater.

In some communities, it is necessary to have an approved three-wire system in professional shops. This calls for 3-hole outlets and 3-prong plugs on the machines. Suitable extensions can be made up to accommodate the new system. In the home shop, this is not a costly or an elaborate system to install, but should be done where electric tools are used frequently.

Get an electrician friend to give you the layout for such a system, or have it done by a professional. You should have a separate connection to the main switch box and a grounded circuit to a separate utility box of outlets. This will assure you of adequate grounding and eliminate the possibility of fuse blowouts affecting the house circuits. You will be less likely to overload the house circuits when the refrigerator, washer, freezer, and other appliances are in operation.

Whatever system you are using for power, inspect the fuses in the fuse box. Never use a fuse that is rated higher than the wiring is designed to carry. Remember that in order for your fire insurance policy on the building and contents to be valid in case of a fire, the wiring system in the building must comply with the Code of the National Board of Fire Underwriters. This code provides that all light and power circuits must be protected by circuit breakers or fuses of correct size. The fuse consists of a short wire or strip of lead alloy which melts at a lower temperature than the copper wire connecting the circuit. When more than a specified amount of current flows through the fuse, the small wire "blows," or melts. For example, a 10-amp. fuse burns out when more than 10 amperes of current flows through it.

Current flowing through a wire meets a resistance which creates heat. The larger the wire, the more current it can carry without heating up excessively. A No. 14 wire will safely carry 15 amperes of current. Therefore, such wiring (which is the size usually found in house circuits) should be protected by a 15-amp. fuse. A circuit of No. 12 wire should have a 20-amp. fuse. The use of oversize fuses is not only a violation of the Electrical Code, but is foolish and reckless—always an invitation to trouble. The 8-inch, Model 108 portable saw and the Model 110 chain saw both pull 10 amps. of current. All the other electric tools described in this book pull less. The router motor pulls 5 amps. The 15-amp. fuse, therefore, is entirely adequate for your shop circuit, provided that it is separate from house utilities. This also assumes that not more than one tool is being used at one time.

The best method of providing a shop outlet is to run a No. 12 or No. 10 wire to a separate connection on the main box, using a BX cable properly and securely grounded. Run this out to the shop work space and connect it to a three- or four-plug fuse box for machine outlets. Use a 20-amp. fuse in the main box behind the separate circuit and use only 15-amp. fuses in the local box. When a fuse does burn out, be sure to find the trouble and remedy the cause before inserting a new fuse.

When any electric tool is put through its regular maintenance examination, you should look out for any exposed or loose wires or damaged insulation. This is particularly important where such exposure can make contact with the frame and cause a short. A hot wire on the loose can be a dangerous instrument besides just causing a blown fuse. Check also to see that the ground-wire connection is secure to the frame of the machine. These sometimes come loose and will then fail to give the proper grounding. In the first place, you should always buy only equipment and electric tools which have been approved by the Underwriters Laboratory. Watch out also around the shop for broken plugs or other connections that have become cracked. Repair such defective parts at once, preferably by replacement. Keep the connecting plugs of extensions off the floor. When working around damp or wet areas, use a good rubber mat or other protecting insulator to stand on. It is a good and accepted practice when working on the open job site to wear a heavy pair of rubbers on the feet. This provides important protection other than that from catching cold. Wet feet are a perfect ground and an invitation to a quick termination of activities.

Safety with the machine. One of the best ways to provide the habit of safety is to consciously think of what could happen to you if the board should slip, the tool fly out, the grinder or bit break off, the cut split open, the end break off, and so on. A chip flying off a grinding wheel can go right through a man's body. An unguarded saw blade is a very effective means of losing fingers or hands. The list is long and the accidents are many. Caution is well repaid and thinking of the possible accidents will enable you to work in a manner that will avoid the mishaps when those unexpected breaks and slips do occur.

We have already mentioned the necessity for using the guards that are provided on all well-made tools. Don't forget that these guards are made for a purpose. These tools were originally designed for professionals and are now being used by professional workmen. A smart-aleck may try to avoid being a "sissy" and get around using them. Such characters don't last long on the job and, all too often, show up at the next hiring with a couple of fingers missing. Make sure that your tool guards are working properly at all times and don't imagine any greater conveniences in not using them.

When changing saw blades, drill bits, sanding pads or belts, router cutters, or sanding disks, make sure not only that the machine is turned off, but pull the plug from the socket. This will prevent any accidental throwing of the machine switch when you are holding the saw blade or tool bit in your hand. When grinding or drilling metal, stone, cement, or other hard materials, wear safety goggles or a face shield. Even a very very small particle of grit can put out an eye or cause a deep face cut.

One of the greatest dangers in using power tools of any kind, and one of the most common causes of accidents, is simple carelessness. A worker becomes so familiar with his job and his tools that he ceases to respect them as he did at the beginning of his apprenticeship. Or he may be in a hurry and will try

short cuts. Too often the guards and protecting devices seem
to get in his way and slow up production. Around many industrial plants, the worker seems to think that the safety engineer
is deliberately plotting ways to cramp his output and slow him
up. As fast as the management can think up means of protecting the worker, the latter will think up ways of evading the
device. Such workers need education and discipline. If the
attitude continues, they should be fired. They are a danger not
only to themselves but to other workers as well.

Another danger is that of loose clothing, ties, torn garments,
and the like, which can catch in the drill or saw. Dress right
for the job. Wear safety shoes to prevent a broken toe or foot
when working around heavy objects. Have a convenient stand
or place to put the tool when it is not being used. Keep it out
of the way and in a safe place. Keep extension cords from
piling up underfoot and on the walk ways.

One important caution should be heeded regarding *all* electric motors and this matter of commutator spark. *NO electric
motor should be started in a room or unventilated area when
there is presence of gasoline, naphtha, or other explosive or
combustible liquids or gases.* For the same reason, such materials should never be used around electric motors. The slight-
est spark of the motor can ignite such gases with vigorous results.

Care of the electric motor. The motor on portable electric
tools is a Universal type which is ordinarily made to operate
only on a single-phase 115 volt, 0 to 60 cycle, AC or DC circuit. *Do not* connect such motors to a 230-volt circuit, for you
will very likely burn out both the armature and field windings.
If you require a heavier current, all of these tools can be
obtained with motors wired for 230-volt lines. This requirement must be specified when you buy the tool and it must be
specified on the data plate of the motor.

The Universal motor uses a series field winding and these
motors develop sparks at the contact of the brushes and the

commutator. Since this is a normal occurrence which can do no harm to either motor or user, it need not cause alarm. If the motor sparking should become noticeably excessive, however, it indicates a rough or dirty commutator. Whatever the cause, the motor should be inspected immediately and the commutator cleaned.

Cleaning the commutator is a simple task and can be done without dismantling the motor housing on those tools that have large air vents placing the commutator within reach. On many of the saws, the drills, and some sanders, the cap of the motor housing must be removed in order to get to the commutator. Once the commutator is exposed or within reach of a flat stick about the length of the first finger, use a narrow strip of commutator paper to brighten the copper surfaces while turning the chuck with the fingers of the other hand. *Do not use emery or aluminum oxide abrasive* for this job. Go to an electric shop and buy a piece of commutator paper. Absolutely nothing else will do. Hold the strip of paper, abrasive side out, folded over the end of the flat stick. Push the end of the stick against the copper surface until the paper holder bends slightly and you have a flat contact rather than an edge contact at the end of the stick.

Move the paper up and down as the commutator is turned by revolving the chuck. Keep this up until you have brightened the entire surface. Now blow out the dust and wipe the copper surface with a clean cloth and a dip of carbon tetrachloride before restoring the motor cap. Try the motor and see if the sparking continues. If it seems normal, all is well. If it still gives out excessive sparks, consult your dealer or your nearest *authorized* service agency.

From time to time the brushes, located on opposite sides of the motor housing, should be inspected for wear. Do not allow the brushes to wear down to less than $\frac{1}{4}$ inch in length. Replace them with new brushes as specified in the machine parts list before they wear any farther. When removing the brushes, be sure to mark the position of the square holders and remember which one came from which side. They must be put back on the proper side and in the same position or they will make an uneven contact.

Keep the motor clean and dry at all times and you'll have little trouble requiring more than ordinary inspection and common-sense care. Don't allow grease or oil to reach the motor.

Sharpening the rotary saw. Caring for the extra saw blades is an easy task but one which should be carefully done. Keep the extra blades in the cardboard case provided with the blade when new, if they are to be carried in the saw box. If the blades are to be kept in the shop, provide a nail with a large head for each blade, placed so that the blade will hang flat against the wall. Wipe each blade with a light film of oil before putting it away. Clean the blade with turpentine if it collects pitch or gum from the wood.

When the blade needs sharpening, do it right away. If the job is put off, the blade will probably not be available when the next one becomes dull. Sharpening the blade is a problem of restoring the teeth to their original shape and condition. In order to do this, however, four things must be done if you choose to do the job yourself. The first step is jointing. In this operation, all the teeth must be ground to the same length. Raise the depth adjustment until the saw teeth are all above the shoe of the saw. Hold the saw so that the shortest tooth barely touches a piece of wood held across the opening in the base. Turn the blade by hand while moving an abrasive stone across each tooth until all of them are exactly the same length. Now remove the blade from the saw.

Setting the teeth is the second step and this job consists of bending the points alternately left and right to provide kerf, or clearance for the saw. Be very careful to set all the teeth by

the same amount so that each will have the same amount of
cutting to do. If one or more teeth are out of line, they will
wear faster than the others and will tend to pull the blade to
left or right of the cutting line. The setting of the teeth can be
done by any of several inexpensive devices now on the market,
or they can be set by block and punch as shown in the photograph. The correct amount of set for average wood sawing is
between 5 and 10 degrees. If the teeth are set too much, the
cut will not be smooth and the blade will cause vibration and
chatter. The set should extend for only one-third of the length
of the tooth.

Sharpening the teeth of the saw is the third step in the
process of reconditioning. Set the saw blade in the vise, holding it with two pieces of plywood cut half round so the ends
will just leave the teeth exposed. The rip-saw teeth are filed
straight across at right angles to the blade. Be careful to
observe the "hook" angle of the teeth on the new blade and
restore each tooth to this original angle as you sharpen. A
half-round, 6-inch mill file is good for sharpening the small
blades. The small end can be used to file the gullet of each
tooth as the work progresses. It is good practice to file the
teeth that are set away from you the first time around. Reverse
the blade and do the same with the alternate teeth.

Back clearance is the angle of narrow surface extending
away from the tip at the back of each tooth. If you will notice
the teeth on the new blade again, you will see that there is a
bit more back clearance away from the point of the tooth than
there is on the saw that you have just jointed. With the flat
side of the file, knock that back-clearance angle down somewhat as shown in the illustration. The fourth and last step of
blade repairing is called gumming. This you may have done as
you sharpened the face of the teeth. If not, use a small half-

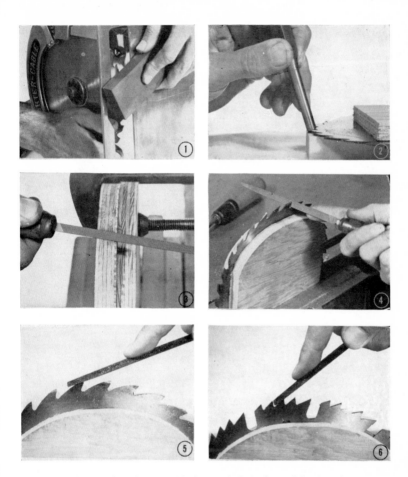

Fig. 40. Sharpening the saw blade. (1) Jointing with abrasive stone. (2) Setting teeth with punch and block. (3) File cross-cut teeth at angle of 10 to 15 degrees. (4) Combination teeth are filed at very small angle. (5) Ripping teeth have small back clearance and narrow gullet. (6) Planer blade has steep clearance and long rakers.

round or rattail file and round out the shape of the gullet between each tooth.

Combination teeth look very much like the rip-saw teeth just described and are sharpened in the same way. Use a slight angle when filing the face of the teeth. The angle of the file should be about 5 to 8 degrees instead of perpendicular as with rip-saw teeth. Cross-cut saw teeth are jointed and set in the same manner as above, but the filing process is different. You will find that the teeth of the new blade are sharpened at an angle of 10 to 15 degrees on the inside of the set. The teeth stick out, leaning forward, of course, at a very sharp angle. The original bevel of the tooth must be retained and it is good practice to hold the file at the same angle, working on alternate teeth and reversing the blade after the first circuit is completed.

The teeth of the planer blade are filed exactly like those of the combination blade. The angle across the face should be about 5 to 8 degrees. The front of the rakers is filed straight across at a 90-degree angle.

The blade will undoubtedly need dressing because it is almost impossible to set all the teeth exactly alike. Put the blade back on the saw arbor and lower the height gage to the full reach of the blade. Stand the saw up on end or turn it over so that the blade is fully exposed when the guard is held back. Now place an abrasive stone flat on the bottom of the saw base alongside the blade and back of its center line so that the stone is just touching the edges of the teeth. Start the motor and bring the teeth into line by letting each of them stroke the stone. This will dress down the tips of those set too far out. Just a slight contact is all that is necessary. The dressing of the teeth should be done before filing.

Grinding twist drills. Earlier in this book we mentioned the various parts of twist drills that are subject to wear and must

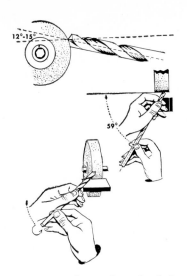

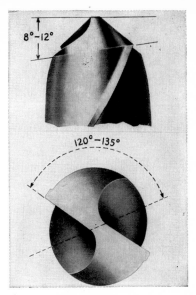

Proper angle to the wheel for lip grinding.

Correct angle of lip clearance, outer edge.

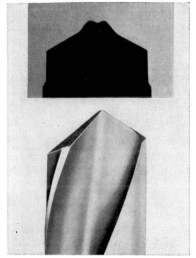

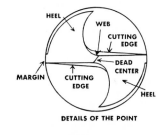

DETAILS OF THE POINT

Wrong—Lips have unequal angle and length.

Thin the web as drill is pointed back.

Cleveland Twist Drill Co.

Fig. 41. Grinding a twist drill.

be frequently inspected. Every time a drill bit has to be worked on, the dead center, point, heel, lip clearance, margin, body clearance, and web must be rechecked. The dead center and the point are not the same thing. The point is the entire cone-shaped surface at the cutting end of the drill. Dead center is the small, sharp edge at the very tip of the point. The dead center is formed by the intersection of the surfaces of the point and must always be in the exact center of the drill. The heel is that portion of the point that slopes back from the cutting edge. The illustration shows these various parts of the drill.

Lip-clearance angle is the angle of clearance to the work just behind the cutting edge. The margin is the narrow, high strip of metal that runs along the edge of the spiral flutes and determines the full diameter of the drill. Body clearance is the distance by which the margin stands out from the body of the drill. The web is the area of metal between the flutes of the drill. It increases in thickness as it rises from the drill point throughout the length of the body.

To get the most satisfactory results when grinding the drill bits, and to get the best results when using them afterward, a drill-grinding fixture is highly recommended. With considerable practice, a good job can be done freehand, but most workmen cannot afford to spend the time in learning this art. To get a good point on the drill, it is necessary that both cutting edges have the same lip angle (usually 59 degrees to the axis of the drill), be exactly the same length, and have the proper clearance, or heel angle. Lip-clearance angle should be from 12 to 15 degrees. If this angle is too small, stresses which are set up when using the drill will cause the metal in the web to split. If the lip angles are not the same, the drill will cut unevenly and will bind in the hole. If the angles are the same, but the lengths are different, the hole will be larger than the drill and the stress on the tool will be very great. If both the angles and lengths of the lips are different, the hole will be larger than the drill for most of its depth and will have an uneven bottom.

Any other defects in the sharpening of the twist drill will cause other defects in workmanship. These troubles can be avoided with a drill-holding fixture. With the drill centered in the V-blocks of the holder, the device is adjusted to the desired angle of cutting edge and the drill is turned until it makes contact with the wheel. If sharpening freehand, hold the drill between thumb and index finger and place the fingers on the tool rest so that the desired angle is formed between the center line of the drill and the face of the wheel. Lower the shank of the drill just a bit and place the heel against the wheel, raising the shank end in a counterclockwise direction as the bit and wheel are brought in contact. Use a drill-tip gage for checking both the length and angle of the tip.

As the point of the drill becomes ground back after repeated sharpening, the web becomes somewhat thicker and the point must be ground down to correct size. Check a new drill of the same diameter and grind the web of the old one down to the same web thickness. It will usually be about $\frac{1}{16}$ of an inch or less.

Keeping other tools in condition. Various portable electric tools need minor repairs occasionally, just as all tools. The best type of care is prevention of trouble by regular and frequent inspection. When any type of trouble does develop, tend to it at once. It is very dangerous to both work and user, as well as other workmen nearby, to try to use broken or damaged tools. If the broken part can be easily replaced, get a new part from your dealer or authorized service repair station. If you don't know what the trouble is or the damage cannot be easily repaired, send the tool away for repairs.

Grinding wheels can be kept in good shape by using an inexpensive facing tool occasionally. If the wheel becomes filled with soft metal or gummed with particles or worn unevenly, hold the facing tool against it while running the wheel and simply "regrind" the working face of the stone. Clogging with soft metal can be remedied by using the wire brush in the electric drill and, with the grinder running, giving the wheel a light work over. Be very careful to inspect the grinding wheels for breakage and never install a wheel that is known to be cracked. The motors of the bench grinder run at very high speed and centrifugal force can split a wheel quickly and with alarming force.

The router-shaper bits are kept sharp by the small grindstone which comes with the basic bit set. Give the cutters a light touch frequently and they should never need a more serious operation. The plane cutting blade can be sharpened quickly on the sharpening device which comes with the complete kit. Here again, a light stoning after any amount of use will keep the blade in first-class shape.

Maintenance on cutting edges other than those used with the portable tools can be quickly done with the abrasive disk and the combo-tool. All types of blades can be sharpened with excellent results in just a few swipes with the rotary abrasive disk. Knives and small cutting tools around the shop or kitchen can be sharpened on the small grinding wheel that comes with the combo-tool kit.

10 ≡ WORKING TECHNIQUE
WITH PORTABLE POWER

Portable power discovered new methods. As more and more workmen in various trades began to use the wonderfully handy tools introduced by portable power, they also found that the advantages were far greater than mere convenience in straight sawing. These tools not only brought the speed and accuracy of machine work right to the job, but they introduced faster and more efficient ways of doing things. This does not mean that the old, established methods of joinery, cabinet-making, and building were outmoded, but it does mean that the method of actual construction and even the procedure of the work was greatly altered.

For instance, the problem of building a cabinet for the kitchen formerly called for careful measuring, drawing up plans, cutting out the parts in the shop, and fitting the sub-assemblies together with hot glue, then removing the sections to the job and setting them together. Today, with plywoods, plastic materials for the top, chrome trim for the edge, and the saw, sander, drill, router, and a pair of sawhorses, the carpenter can set up right in the kitchen or on the back porch and do the job in much less time.

The technique of joining pieces of wood together in a professional manner was, until fairly recently, a mystery to the layman. It was exclusively the possession of the expert carpenter and the advanced woodworker who had spent some years in the practice of his trade. Making the precise joints of the cabinet- and furniture maker was a difficult job with ordinary hand tools and an untrained hand. The ease and accuracy with which portable power tools can do these jobs has been described in the foregoing pages of this book. A little practice with the techniques shown will make work of professional quality available to almost every worker, professional as well as home shop amateur. In addition, the many drawings of things to make, details of various projects, the "how to" of books and magazines which are now so popular have made limitless information available to everyone. With reliable and accurately built power tools, the average workman can turn out products with the same professional-type joints and finishes. He can use different and simpler methods of obtaining the same result. He can cut accurate joints the first time and put pieces together without tedious and careful planing. The process of making the joint, however, may be quite different from that used by the master craftsman using hand tools.

Plan and organize your work. The most efficient way to start any task is to plan the work, organize the tools and materials, and decide on the logical procedure to follow. This does not always mean that the steps should be put down in a one-two-three-four fashion. When working with power tools especially, the job should be broken up so that all similar parts can be cut, drilled, sanded, routed, or shaped at one time. It is always best to start with the plan of the work drawn to scale and carefully marked for measurement. Cut all the plywood parts at one time. Cut the straight pieces of stock at the same time. Where there is more than one piece of the same length, cut them together or with the aid of a gage or jig. When holes have to be drilled, put the pieces aside and do the marking and drilling at one time. Such a system will speed up the work and make for greater accuracy. If in doubt as to how you should proceed with a particular joint or section of the job, use a piece of scrap material and make a trial cut and fitting. It takes only a few minutes and it will save much good material and many headaches. Once you have mastered a particular joint, it will give you no further trouble.

When you get to the problem of making the actual joints that you have decided to use, consider the working characteristics of the saws, the plane, and the router and decide which of these tools you should use. A simple saw cut followed by the hand chisel may be entirely sufficient. You may want to use the saw followed by the router. You may decide to do the job entirely with the router. There is no established rule that dictates the use of any particular tool in any given situation. The choice has to be yours and based on plain common sense coupled with your knowledge of what the tool can do and what you can do with it. Some types of joints may be done in several different ways. Plan which methods you are going to use. Try them out and be sure they work.

Using the guides and templets. In the chapters dealing with the drills, saws, and the router, considerable emphasis was given to the construction and use of various cross-cut, or cut-off, guides, drill templets, routing and shaping forms, patterns, and templets. These shop-made tools are not only a frequent necessity for doing many types of jobs, but are a permanent convenience in future work. Some time spent in making these accessories properly and accurately will save much time in later work, whenever similar tasks come up. The cross-cut and ripping guides for the portable saw will be used repeatedly. It is wise, therefore, to make them of good material, fasten them securely at the joining, keep the edges smooth and free of cuts

and dents, and hang them up out of the way and in a safe place
when not in use.

Drill templets may not seem so important, but certain ones
will be used frequently. Make them of oak or straight-grained
chestnut, particularly those used for screw holes joining table
and cabinet tops to the frame from the underside. The strips
used are usually ¾ inch wide, the screws used are usually No.
10. The holes drilled in the templet should be, for shank clearance, No. 10 of the numbered drills, or ³⁄₁₆ inch of the fractional-size drills. Use the doweling jig or similar device for
making these holes and place them exactly three inches apart,
center to center. In large table tops, only every other hole
need be used. In smaller work, all may be needed. In any case,
the templet, when made about 12 or 15 inches long, will serve
in locating and drilling the holes quickly and accurately.

We have already stressed the importance of making the
router-shaper templets and guides accurately. This factor con-
tributes more than any other, unless it be that of sharp cutting
bits, to doing good work with the portable router. Use plenty
of time in planning and constructing the templet and the job
itself will be easy. Each time a good guide or templet is made
for a particular job, shape, or pattern, it means that the difficulties of doing that particular job have been eliminated for the
future. Mark the templet to show the job description, dimensions, spacing of fingers, curves, etc., and put it away safely for
future use.

In this connection, it is a good idea to keep shop notes of
any particular problems that are encountered and the methods,
fixtures, and tools used to overcome them. A wealth of useful
shop experience can be quickly accumulated in this way and
future problems reduced thereby. Useful shop hints and how-
to-do-it suggestions can be gained from the many popular

Fig. 42. Handy shop helps to speed work. (1) Use the opposite part of joint to check cutter width. (2) A sample joint can be used to set machine for duplication. (3) Hold handle of plane down when nearing the end of board. (4) Clamp a parallel edge to guide router when making straight edge. (5) Insert a felt pad under sander shoe for making hump. (6) Hump in sander provides faster working on high spots.

monthly magazines dealing with shop and construction problems.

Miscellaneous shop notes. PREVENTING SPLINTERING. In sawing, drilling, or routing operations, splintering of the material as the cut reaches the edge (when working across the grain) is a frequent problem. The best way to eliminate this is by use of a backing piece or scrap material held tightly to the opposite side or edge of the work. The tool will then cut into the scrap material and not splinter the edge or face of your work. Sometimes this trouble can be avoided by stopping the cut before the opposite side or edge is reached, turning the material over or around, and finishing from the other side.

ODD JOBS FOR THE DRILL STAND. When set up on the drill stand, the ¼-inch drill can be used for jobs other than driving wood bits and twist drills. Any of the router or shaper bits with a ¼-inch shank, or attached to the adapter, will fit in the drill chuck. The end-cutting straight bits, grooving bits, core box, or dovetail bits can be used for such jobs as countersinking, edge notching, sinking holes for bolt heads or nuts, mortising for joints, and any small jobs where a router setup is not warranted and where the cut is in light or soft wood which the drill motor and speed can handle. Many times the delicacy of the job requires a slower speed and careful guiding of the work. This is quite possible by using the drill stand and the base of the stand to steady the work and guiding it with both hands.

GREATER SPEED IN HOUSE FRAMING. Saving work time in house or general building construction means saving the greatest part of the cost. Lower costs in house building are not gained by using less or cheaper material (although this may sometimes seem to be the case). Good builders save costs by better planning and utilization of labor. Prefabrication is most often a matter of delivering yard lumber to the builder's shop, where the studs, joists, and rafters are cut to length, notched, and marked for quick erection by sections. The big builders can handle materials much better this way. The smaller units, however, can gain the same advantages by having the lumber delivered to the site, one man on the job doing all the cutting with the portable saw. Give such a man a half-day start and he can keep ahead of any four-man crew in cutting and notching an ordinary house frame. Naturally, he can work faster with a helper to aid in handling and setting up the pieces to be cut. Furthermore, he should be a man with some experience in framing. On a one- or two-man job, however, it is necessary only to find the right length for studs and joists and the proper end angles and notches for rafters. One piece can be used as a pattern and the rest cut out quickly with the electric portable saw.

REMOVING PAINT FOR REFINISHING. The belt sander works best for these jobs, although the wire brush should be used for the loose particles and blistered areas. Only open-coated abrasives should be used on the sander and, even then, short pull-back strokes have to be used to prevent clogging. Any prolonged working in one area will heat and soften the paint. Keep the sander moving with short strokes. For reducing the high spots and especially thick areas of paint, a felt pad about 1½ inches wide can be inserted under the shoe to form a hump. This reduces the contact area but is an advantage.

Additional helps for the table saw. In chapter 4, the saw table for adapting the portable saw to standard circular saw operations was described. Adding this valuable tool to the workshop of portable machines opens a very wide field of sawing operations, particularly for small work, interior cabinets, moldings, furniture, built-in equipment, and parts that would be difficult to handle with the portable saw used in the normal manner. Describing some of the various helps and methods used with the table saw will give a better understanding of the work this accessory can do.

THE RIP FENCE. Running from front to back across the top of the table is a bar called the rip fence. This guide is adjusted and fastened in place by a large hand screw at the very front of the table. An additional screw hook at the back end is used to clamp the fence securely in place. This bar can be moved to any location on the table parallel to the line of the blade and is used for ripping cuts. The material is guided along its face and into the blade, which should be set so that it clears the top of the wood by about 3/8 inch. The back edge of the wood must be straight in order to get a straight cut in ripping. Push the end of the material up to the blade before starting the motor and make sure the cut will be where wanted. When working short or narrow pieces, use a pusher stick (or sticks) and keep the fingers away from the blade. Keep the board firmly against the guide fence and use a steady push, along a straight line.

CROSS CUTTING. Pieces that are over 3 feet long can best be handled with the portable saw held in the hand. The saw table is excellent for cross cutting short pieces and for cutting joints. The cross-cut guide, or angle gage, slides across the table from front to back in a groove that is to the left of the blade (from the operator's position). The head of the angle gage is fastened to this slide bar with a knurled screw and graduated segment. At 90 degrees, this guide head is exactly perpendicular to the line of the saw blade. It can be adjusted to any other angle for angle sawing. The best procedure for cross cutting is to hold the material firmly against the guide with the left hand and use the right hand for advancing the guide past the blade. This gives a steady movement and complete control of the cutting. It also places the operator to one

Fig. 43. Help for table sawing technique. (1) Pusher and holding sticks. (2) Feather board for ripping. (3) Stop block for cross cutting. (4) Jig for tapered cuts. (5) Angle guide for compounds. (6) Saw cuts for lap joints.

side of the line of the blade and avoids the possibility of being hit if a cut-off piece should be thrown by the saw.

A stop block is a good device to use when cutting off with the angle gage. This block should be clamped to the rip fence just forward of the saw blade. The material is measured up against the block, then held firmly against the angle gage. When advanced to the saw blade, the work cannot bind between the blade and the rip fence. This method is also accurate and fast for cutting duplicate lengths and making various joints.

ANGLE SAWING. The most common angle made with the saw is the 45-degree cut for mitering. For this operation, the angle gage is set to either side, as the angle may require, and the material held firmly against it. Make the sawing pass slowly and firmly because the material has a tendency to pull in or push out, depending on which way the gage is angled. Make a test cut with scrap wood when sawing any degree of angle. The settings are manual and only careful test and measurement will assure complete accuracy. It is also good business to use only the cross-cut or planer blade for all angle and miter cuts. When cutting to a mark, advance the wood right up to the blade and inspect carefully the point where the teeth contact the material. Adjust the position of the board until the contact is in the right place. Now hold the material firmly in place against the cut-off guide, turn on the motor, and make the cut. Compound angles are a simple matter with the portable saw used on the saw table. Adjust the angle of the saw from underneath the table, using the same angle gage that was used in hand sawing. The table angle gage furnishes the miter angle.

GROOVES, RABBETS, AND DADOES. In short or narrow pieces of wood, these cuts may be made quickly and easily on the saw table. Set the rip fence close to the blade and measure the position carefully so that the blade will cut exactly to the width of the rabbet. Lower the blade so that the topmost teeth will just rake the width mark. For instance, to cut a rabbet ½ inch by ½ inch, the blade should be just ½ inch above the table and the rip fence just far enough away so that, including the kerf, the cut will be ½ inch from the face. Now make the first cut with the material face down on the table and the end or edge firmly against the rip fence. Be sure to make the pass all the way across the high part of the blade. The second cut is made with the back of the piece held firmly against the fence. Grooves and dadoes are best made with the work held against the angle gage. Cut the extreme ends of the cross-grain cuts for gains and dadoes before making the passes in between. Again, the work should be moved up to the blade for careful checking before starting the motor. Make sure the blade is adjusted for the correct height and pass the work all the way across the blade before lifting it up and returning for the next pass.

TAPER SAWING. Table and bench legs often call for tapered cuts which can be made with the saw table and the use of a very simple jig. To prepare the jig, lay out the lines of the taper on a piece of scrap wood. Mark the lines clearly and cut the piece out by using the rip blade and a long rip guide such as that described in chapter 4. This can be done most accurately by using the portable saw held in the hand and guided by the long rip gage or a guide piece clamped to the board. Cut the wide end of the tapered jig on the saw table, making a right angle to one of the sides. Nail a flat strip across this wide end. Now the jig can be placed against the rip fence, small end leading, and the work material placed against the tapered side of the jig and in front of the tail block. The tail piece will push the wood into the blade as the jig is guided forward. All four legs of the table can be quickly cut out with the same jig. Square stock can be tapered on two sides by the same method.

THE FEATHER BOARD. A very useful implement can be made for the saw table in a few minutes which is both a safety device and an aid in keeping work against the rip fence. Use a piece of ½-inch stock, about 5 inches by 14 inches. Cut off one end at an angle of 30 degrees and make a series of saw cuts at this edge ¼ inch apart and lengthwise of the board for about half its length. This piece can be clamped to the edge of the table as shown in the illustration for steadying the stock while ripping, cutting tenons, etc.

Joints and cabinetwork. Good joints are the mark of a good wood craftsman. It is not necessary to be able to make every joint in the book, but several of them must be mastered so that necessary alternatives can be used for different types of work. The most common types of joints used in woodworking are shown here in the illustration. Several of them have been discussed and explained in previous chapters of this book. It is worth while to consider them as a group and look at the different ways in which these joints are used and how they can best be made with portable tools.

LAP JOINTS. These joints make up a very large family of cabinetmaking connections, the distinguishing feature of which is a cutout on each side so that two parts overlap each other to make a fit of the same thickness as the parts being joined. These joints are strong and easily made with either the portable saw, the router, or the table saw. They are sometimes called halved joints because standard practice cuts away half the thickness from each section. These joints are much used in skeleton framework of tables, desks, cabinets, and paneling. Methods for construction have been shown in chapters 4 and 7.

TONGUE AND GROOVE. This is the common flooring, outside wall sheathing, and roofing-board joint for making a

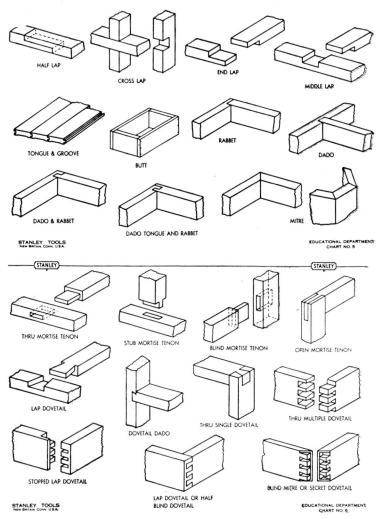

Fig. 44. Common wood joints.

continuous and smooth surface. On such material as this, the parts are cut at the mill. Shelving, cabinet ends, and table tops, however, are often put together with this type of joint and, when properly glued and smoothed, make an excellent joint for large surfaces. This joint is easily made on the shaper table.

BUTT JOINTS. These are the most common types of joints in which one piece butts up against another. The chief requirement of making this joint is that of straight cutting. The side that does the butting is simply cut across at 90 degrees and sanded to fit flush against the other part. The other side may be plain, notched as a rabbet when joined at the edge or corner, or notched as a dado when joined somewhere along the length of a piece. The cutting of these parts was described in chapters 4 and 7. They are easily cut with either saw or router.

MITER JOINTS. The molding-corner, or picture-frame, joint is more easily made on the saw table with the planer blade. This joint is especially useful when joining two pieces along the flat edge. Variations for fastening are many. The splined miter is shown in the illustration and is very easy to cut by using the same table adjustment for both sides. The grain of the piece that is slipped into the cut should be perpendicular to that of the joining sides. Use hardwood for the spline. Inside blocks or nails through the corners can also be used when the joint is concealed.

MORTISE AND TENONS. The tenons can be cut as previously explained, with the saw or router. The mortise side should be laid out only after the tenon is cut. The end of the tenon should be used to mark the opening into which it goes. The cutout can be done with the router and straight bit, with the corner chisel used for squaring up the corners. There are several variations of this joint, depending on the location of the work where it is needed. It can be cut through, stub, blind, or

Fig. 45. Making joints with the portable saw and table saw. (1) Open tongue and tenon are cut to depth on shoulder. (2) Parts must fit squarely together without force. (3) Splined miter is cut the same way on both sides. (4) Parts fit snugly over spline insert. (5) Dovetail dado calls for angle and depth setting. (6) Straight cut and chisel to clean the corners make the insert side.

open, depending chiefly on the final appearance and whether it is on a corner or mid-section of a part. These four types are very widely used in cabinetwork and furniture construction. They are very strong when made to fit close and properly glued.

LAP AND DADO DOVETAIL. These joints are very similar to the simpler ones described before, with the exception of the angled side or edge. This feature makes for a stronger combination, especially when used on small constructions and when closely fitted. They should always be tight enough to hold securely without glue or screws, although additional fastening is almost always used.

DOVETAILS. The through, stopped, lap, and secret dovetails are the principal varieties of this very useful joint, each having its particular uses. The through joint can be used at any corner joining where final appearance is no problem. The stopped lap is best for outside surfaces where both ends must be concealed. The lap, or half-blind, is used on drawer fronts where only one side need be concealed. The blind miter is a very fancy, concealed corner joint which is perhaps the final examination in making good cabinet joinery. Making these joints is a simple job for the router and the finger gage described in chapter 7.

One final suggestion. When approaching the problem of what joint to use and how to make it, look first at the stresses that will be placed on that particular part. This will suggest the degree and direction of resistance that the joint must have. Once the type has been selected, appearance must be considered and the method of cutting will be much simplified. Make a trial run first out of scrap material and make sure the parts fit closely.

11 ≡ WOOD
AND WOOD PRODUCTS

Since wood and wood products are the materials used chiefly with portable power tools, it is worth while to include a chapter on them. A workman should know something about the raw materials he uses, and in no trade is there a greater variety of products available than in the woodworking field. In addition to some seventy different natural woods sold generally, there are ten or fifteen useful varieties of wood by-products that have found a market. The number of such materials is increasing each year.

In general, there is no particular problem encountered when using portable power tools on these various materials. The speed of the machine and the efficiency of the blades and bits make the working of all these products comparatively easy. In the chapters on the drill, saw, and router some differences were noted in the technique for handling soft and hardwoods and wood products. Tool edges and teeth must always be sharp for portable power tools, but this is particularly important when cutting or drilling the hardwoods. Differences in technique may seem to be unimportant to the beginner, but they make the difference between professional workmanship and an indifferent job. Learning to work with different woods is largely a matter of experience. In this chapter, we will look at some of the different qualities of woods and explain how the materials of the shop are marketed and sold by the dealer.

General qualities of wood and wood products. You may have heard some people say, "They don't make houses today like they used to," or "Somehow, the wood we get today isn't what it used to be." Both statements are very true, but usually not in the sense that the speaker had in mind at the time. What he said was right, but what he meant was wrong.

Today and for several years, excepting the period of emergency building and fast cutting and marketing of wood during the last war, we have produced better lumber and built better houses than we ever did before. We have better materials for building, better design, greater efficiency, and better workmanship. Standardization both in the lumber industry and in the building trades has brought about a better selection and use of materials. We no longer build with whatever is available on the corner lot or at the local sawmill.

More efficient mill practices have improved the preparation of lumber and have found uses for nearly all the by-products. The chips and sawdust are now made into several types of fiberboard. These materials are sometimes harder and stronger than the wood from which they are made. Plywoods are made from several types of wood and given finish surfaces of almost every variety. The sheets are thinner, stronger, made in larger sizes, not subject to shrinkage or warping, checking or splitting, and are far more useful than the lumber from which they are made. In the forest, trees are grown to maturity before cutting. Selective methods eliminate the culls and harvest the better trees at the right time. Wood is prepared better at the mill, better seasoned and machined, and is marketed with better standards in quality and size than it formerly was.

Structure and characteristics of wood. The way in which wood is formed in nature has a lot to do with its uses and working qualities in the shop. When we cut down a tree and slice the log into sections of lumber, we can see that wood grows both vertically and in width, or girth, of the tree. In the cross section of the log we see a number of circles forming a more or less uniform pattern around a center core. Near

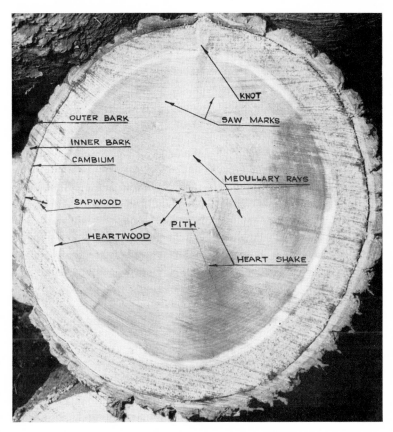

Fig. 46. Cross section of an oak log.

the center these rings are somewhat closer together and are usually darker in color. If we test the wood in this central area, we find that it is harder than the lighter wood in the outer part of the log.

The split section of the tree, too, shows that the wood grows in slivers or fibers that run lengthwise of the trunk. If we examine these fibers with a magnifying glass, we will see that they are composed of minute cells of varying sizes and thickness. It is the thickness of the walls of these cells that determines the weight and strength of the wood and the uses to which it can be put.

Looking at the cross section of the tree trunk again, we find an outside shell which is called the outer bark. Just inside of that is a thinner layer of soft and moist material called the inner bark. This section carries the food material made in the leaves to all live parts of the tree. Beneath the inner bark is a thin and darker layer, the cambium, in which the wood cells as well as the bark cells are formed for growth. Next comes a thicker section of light-colored wood which is known as the sapwood. This part of the tree trunk is the living part of the wood that carries the sap from the roots to the leafy sections. The largest section of darker wood is the heartwood of the tree. This is the inactive part of the wood which has been pressed more solidly by the annual growth of the trunk and has become the harder and more durable part of the wood. The annual layers of growth are shown by the thin, concentric rings which begin at the very center and continue outward to the bark. Through these growth rings, extending from the pith and out through the heartwood, are thin lines called medullary rays or wood rays, which function in transferring food throughout the tree trunk. Splits that sometimes occur in radiating lines from the center of the tree are called heartshakes. These are defects associated with decay at the center of the trunk.

If a tree is cut too early in its life, it doesn't have much heartwood. While both sapwood and heartwood are about equal in strength, the heartwood has better working qualities, is better in appearance, and is more durable. The sapwood will absorb preservatives to a greater extent and is much better for outdoor use with such treating processes. A mature tree ready to be cut for lumber will have a large area of heartwood that can be cut into lumber for various purposes.

If we look closely at the individual bands of wood in each section marked by the annual growth rings, we will find that there is a difference from light to dark in the color of the fibers. The light-colored portion is the part that has grown in the spring. The darker section is the summer or autumn wood. The ratio of the portions of springwood and summerwood are very important to the strength and other characteristics of the wood. Generally, the varieties which grow rapidly and form wide growth rings having a large percentage of springwood, are coarse grained and not as strong as the slower-growing trees having narrow growth bands and denser summerwood.

Upon examining different types of wood, we also find that some have fibers that grow straight and parallel to the bark. In others, the fibers seem to run in many directions or at an angle with the sides of the lumber. The two types are designated as straight grained and cross grained. We can readily see that it makes a difference how the logs are cut into lumber if we expect to get the best grain and strength qualities from the wood. The sawing method that produces the best lumber is called quartersawing in the hardwoods and rift-sawing in softwoods. Both require cutting the log as nearly as possible along radius lines to the center. Wood cut in this manner shows annual ring marks at an angle of 45 degrees or more to the wide face of the board. Such pieces shrink more evenly and have less tendency to twist and warp than those cut by other methods. When the lumber is cut so that the rings are parallel to the flat side or up to 45 degrees to the wide face, it is called flat sawed, plain sawed, or slash sawed. Bastard sawing is midway between the two. Lumber that is flat sawed will curl and warp in the drying and shrinking process. The appearance of the grain of the wood varies greatly with the different methods of cutting.

Varieties of wood and their uses. For strictly botanical reasons, wood from the needle-leaved coniferous trees is called softwood. That from the broad-leaved deciduous trees which shed their leaves each year is called hardwood. These terms do not refer to the working hardness or softness of the wood because some of the softwoods, such as southern pine and fir, are harder than many of the hardwoods. Poplar and basswood are in the hardwood groups yet are among the softest woods in working qualities. By far, the greatest bulk of wood for all commercial purposes comes from the softwood group. The hardwoods are more generally used for furniture, trim, flooring, and cabinetwork. They are known as porous woods and are more difficult to season properly and to use in the shop than are most of the softwoods.

Since the working quality of various woods is of prime importance to the woodworker, a general comparison of the relative softness and hardness of the commonly used woods will be of help in selecting material for any particular project. Of the softwoods, those that are easiest to work with are the western pines and the cedars. The softwoods that have medium working qualities are the hemlocks, white fir, spruce, cypress, and redwood. The most difficult woods of the softwood group are the southern pines, larch, and Douglas fir.

Of the hardwoods, chestnut, poplar, butternut, and basswood are considered very easy to work with hand tools. Walnut, birch, gum, and sycamore are considered to be only of medium difficulty. The heavier hardwoods which are the most difficult to work are the oaks, hickory, beech, maple, birch, locust, elm, cherry, and ash. The latter group contains the most desirable hardwoods, along with walnut and birch, for strength and appearance qualities in making good furniture. This information is all compiled in table 1 in the appendix.

A particular wood that is soft and easy to cut and to shape in the shop is also easily dented and damaged in use. Woods such as oak, maple, and birch are highly useful because of their toughness and durability. In using a particular wood, consider the use and abuse that the article will have to withstand. White pine, ponderosa pine, sugar pine, red cedar, and spruce are excellent material for decorative work, trim, doors, shelving, cabinets, and structural work. These woods are too soft, however, for flooring, worktables, or other work that has to take constant wear. These woods are also too soft to use as structural parts where bolts, screws, or nails are likely to be pulled or worked loose because of strain and stress of the member. When wood is needed that is tough and strong, yet elastic and springy, use hickory or ash.

For general outdoor use, whether painted or not, the cedars, cypress, and redwood wear the longest and have the least tendency to be affected by weather. Any of the other woods have to be well protected with paint or varnish when exposed in any way to the elements.

When we consider the working qualities of wood to be used in the shop, we have to choose material that will take and hold the types of fasteners and joinery needed in the project. For instance, we could not use yellow pine or cedar for small pieces that have to be nailed into place. These woods split too easily. Douglas fir, although it is one of the strongest woods we have, has a tendency to check and split easily and is also subject to shrinking and swelling with changes of humidity.

When a superior finish is needed for furniture and cabinet-work, we have a wide variety of colors and textures and grain figures to choose from among the hardwoods and the imported woods from other countries. The imported woods are most often used as veneers over less-expensive material. They are becoming more generally available, however, and have many desirable qualities for shop projects. They can be bought in either veneer or solid pieces from the larger metropolitan lumber yards or the craft and wood-service shops that advertise for mail-order business.

How to buy lumber. Before buying lumber from the local lumber dealer or the mail-order supply house, one should know something about the general grading and finishing of yard and specialty lumber. Availability of any particular wood in sufficient quantity and grade, or quality, is perhaps of first importance. The character of the wood, its color, strength, durability, and finishing qualities in relation to the project on which it is to be used also have to be considered. Cost is always another important factor in the selection of lumber and the cost will be determined not only by the type of lumber and the sizes needed, but the grade of a particular wood that can be used.

Lower grades of lumber are always cheaper in price than the higher grades. It is often possible to save money in buying lumber by using a lower grade of wood or a higher grade of a cheaper wood. A particular piece of lumber can often be up-graded by careful selection and cutting out the imperfections of a low-grade board. When the sizes of lumber are considered, it is often possible to use a better grade of cheaper wood to better advantage than a lower grade of costly wood. The imperfections, such as knots, splits, stains, coarse grain, or sap, may or may not affect the strength or usability of the piece, depending on their location. These things determine the grade at which the lumber is classified at the mill.

Lumber grading in general follows a nationally accepted standard of quality. Softwoods are graded somewhat along the following lines:

Select, suitable for natural finishes:
  Grade A allows only few and small defects.
  Grade B allows a few blemishes or defects.

Finish, suitable for paint finishes:
  Grade C allows a limited number of defects that can be covered with paint.
  Grade D allows any number of blemishes or defects that do not detract from the appearance when painted.

Common:
  Numbers 1 and 2 must be suitable for use without waste. These grades must be sound lumber, but may have knots and other defects within limits.
  Number 3, 4, and 5 grades permit waste, number 3 allowing larger and coarser defects and some knot holes. The last grade has only the qualification that the wood holds together under ordinary handling.

Hardwood lumber grading follows along the same lines but uses more groupings based on board size limits and the percentage of clear-face cuttings possible. The general designations, in order, are: First, Second, Select, Number 1 Common, Number 2 Common, Sound wormy, and Numbers 3A and 3B Common.

Lumber is sold by the board foot and is designated by the lumber yard in standard yard sizes. Standard widths are multiples of 1 inch, thickness is in quarter-inch increment above

1 inch. Standard lengths are multiples of 2 feet running from 10 to 24 feet. When any particular stock is planed or "dressed," it will be designated by its original standard dimension and the letters D1S or D2S or D4S depending on whether the piece has been dressed on 1, 2, or 4 sides. The dressing process naturally reduces the actual thickness and width of the lumber, usually about $\frac{1}{8}$ to $\frac{3}{16}$ inch on each side. A standard 1×7, D4S, will measure $\frac{25}{32}$ inch in thickness and about $6\frac{1}{2}$ inches in width. The board-foot price for each grade and type of lumber is translated into running-foot price for each standard size. When you order lumber that has to be culled or ripped from larger pieces, the yard usually charges for the standard size of material. You pay for waste stock as well as for the labor of cutting.

Wider boards are always more expensive than the narrow stock so that when plans are made for wide pieces, the cost and labor of gluing must be considered. Another cost factor in ordering any quantity of lumber is choice of width and length. Random width and length will be cheaper than the specified sizes. In any case, it will be rewarding to pay a visit to the lumberyard and become acquainted with the sizes, grades, types of wood, and methods of handling. In choosing the material for any particular project, talk it over with the dealer. He will usually be able to make some suggestions that will save you money and time.

Types and uses of plywoods. Plywood is strictly a modern twentieth-century wood product and a great material for the home workshop as well as for general building purposes. Plywood is all wood and is made of several layers of veneers, or plies, glued together so that the grain of each layer is at right angles to the adjacent layers. An odd number of layers is used, the center ply being called the core and the outer plies being called faces. The core and faces are laid so that the grain runs lengthwise of the panel. The intermediate layers which run across the panel are called cross bands. This banding gives an equal strength quality along the length and width of the panel and gives the material a greater dimensional stability and resistance to checking and splitting. In addition to strength and wear qualities, plywood has the great advantage of size over ordinary wood. Sheets are made in standard 4-foot widths and lengths from 6 to 12 feet.

Plywood is available almost everywhere in standard 3-, 5-, and 7-ply of ¼-, ⅜-, ½-, ¾-, ⅞-, and 1-inch thicknesses. Thicker panels are available for special purposes. The principal wood used in making plywood is Douglas fir. Several hardwoods and some imported woods are now used as facing materials for plywoods. These are particularly useful in cabinets, desks, tables, wall paneling, and even as finish flooring. Special texture and grain faces are also made for unusual decorative purposes.

Two types of plywood are made, both using the same wood, but quite different in weather-resisting qualities. The general interior-type of material cannot be used outdoors or for projects that will be subject to humidity. Special moisture-proof bonding is applied on outdoor plywoods and these must be used for projects such as bathroom cabinets or paneling where moisture is a factor. All plywood is identified as interior or exterior type.

Plywood requires no special tools or techniques for working in the shop. It can be used almost anywhere that ordinary wood is called for, even glued together for obtaining thick pieces, squares, etc. as structural members. Sawing plywood requires a 10-point crosscut hand saw or a combination blade on the power saw. Always cut plywood to the best face. In hand sawing, the good side should be up. For hand power sawing, it must be face down.

In addition to the hardwood and special wood faces now available on plywoods, other types of faces, such as paper plastic, hardboard, cloth plastic, sheet metals, and both clear and colored plastic materials, are being marketed on both ornamental and special purpose plywoods. These special faces have many unusual qualities and are very useful for counter and table tops, bathroom and playroom walls, toys, screens, ornamental doors, and modern furniture. Many rich, solid colors and patterns are available with the plastic-faced plywoods.

Related wood products. Several types of wood fiberboard materials have been on the market for several years. Many of these materials have been greatly improved in working qualities, strength, color, and texture so that today the hardboards, pulpboards, and other rigid-board wood products fill a great variety of needs in the shop.

Masonite is probably the best known of the rigid hardboards. It is available in a lighter colored and softer form as well as the tempered material. Both this and the Weldwood hardboard of the United States Plywood Corporation can be handled just like wood panels in the shop. This material has no grain and is very resistant to cracking, chipping, splintering, and denting. These hardboards can be used with natural finishes or they will serve very well with no finish at all. When used with wood framing, they take all paints, varnishes, and enamels perfectly so that blending the different types of materials is no problem at all. The commercial sizes of sheets available are $\frac{1}{8}$ inch to $\frac{1}{4}$ inch in thickness and 4 feet wide by 6 to 14 feet long.

One of the newest wood-product materials to come on the market is Novoply. This is a completely different material made and sold by the United States Plywood Corporation. It is composed of laminated sheets of wood chips and other bonded wood substances. It can be handled like plywood when machining and joining. A wide variety of finishes is possible and the edges can be filled with a special putty to eliminate the "sandwich" effect common to plywood. It is particularly useful for sliding doors, built-in furniture, and cabinets.

Both rigid boards and flexible sheets that are made for the building industry for structural and insulating purposes often have a use in the shop. These are made from a wide variety of materials including cork, wheat straw, gypsum, kapok, shredded paper, and limestone. Many of these products are made with "tile" faces or imitation leather faces and come in a range of colors. Some of them are useful only for special purposes, such as sound or thermal insulation. Others have excellent possibilities in shop projects and it would be rewarding to visit the local materials dealer and become acquainted with these modern wood substitutes.

APPENDIX

TABLE 1

Work and Use Characteristics of Common Woods

COMMON NAME	CLASS ^{a}	WORK QUALITY ^{b}	WEIGHT ^{c}	BASIC STRESS ^{d}	GENERAL USES	OTHER QUALITIES
Alder, red	H	easy	28	n.d.	Turning, furniture.	Fairly durable in water. Takes good finish.
Ash, white	H	hard	41	2250	Tool handles, furniture, oars.	Light and strong. Paints easily.
Basswood	H	easy	26	n.d.	Venetian blinds, cheap furniture, rules, carving.	Has lustrous finish. Long wearing wood.
Beech	H	hard	45	2400	Interior trim, steam bending, woodenware.	Very tough. Stains evenly almost any color. Satin finish.
Birch, yellow	H	hard	44	2400	Furniture and flooring, cabinet-work, trim.	Excellent finishing qualities, hard and durable. Widely used.
Butternut (white walnut)	H	easy	27	n.d.	Veneer, inlay, small carvings and furniture.	Soft and weak. Takes paint very well.

Name	Class[a]	Work quality[b]	Weight[c]	Basic stress[d]	Uses	Remarks
Cedar, Alaska	S	easy	31	1750	Cabinetwork, boats, doors, blinds, trim.	Splits easily, soft and brittle. Highly decay resistant.
Cedar, western red	S	easy	23	1450	Shingles, siding, ext. trim, boats, novelties, etc.	Same as above. Takes paint well. Good nail holding quality.
Cedar, northern white	S	easy	22	1200	Shingles, tanks, caskets, instruments, boats, fence posts, etc.	Same as above. Even greater resistance to decay.
Cedar, southern white	S	easy	23	1200	Same as northern white cedar.	
Cedar, Port Orford	S	medium	29	1750	Shingles, siding, chests, int. trim, lawn furniture.	Very uniform texture. Spicy odor. Takes paint very well.
Cherry, black	H	hard	35	n.d.	Patterns, small articles, carving.	Very tough and close grained.

[a] Class: *H* denotes hardwood, the deciduous or broad-leaved tree furnishing wood of porous quality; *S*, soft wood, of the coniferous, or evergreen, trees.

[b] Work quality: graded as easy to work, medium hard, or hard to work, as based on the general reputation of the wood among workmen and wood users.

[c] Weight: pounds per cubic foot of air-dry wood with 12 per cent moisture content. This is a comparative table.

[d] Basic stress: a comparative table of load limits in pounds per square inch for bending parallel to the grain and under normal conditions. Woods noted as n.d. are not determined for this load factor. For computing load limits of spans or beams, other considerations have to be made which are too advanced and complicated to include here. Tables and formulas are published by the National Lumber Manufacturers Association, Washington, D. C., for all computations of wood structural design data. The table shown here is for comparison of basic stress limits of the woods listed.

COMMON NAME	CLASS [a]	WORK QUALITY [b]	WEIGHT [c]	BASIC STRESS [d]	GENERAL USES	OTHER QUALITIES
Chestnut	H	easy	30	1500	Flooring, trim, shingles, furniture.	Straight and open grain. Needs filler for painting.
Cottonwood (poplar)	H	medium	26	n.d.	Pulpwood and woodenware.	Light and soft texture, but tough.
Cypress	S	medium	32	2100	Tanks and vats, gutters, siding, shingles and trim.	Very resinous and greasy. Highest resistance to rot.
Elm, rock	H	hard	35	2400	Heavy timbers, framework, steam bending parts.	Very tough and close grained. Excellent natural finish.
Fir, white	S	medium	27	1750	House framing, trim, plywood, sash, boxes, millwork. Greatest market value.	Has little color. Low resistance to decay. Needs filler.
Fir, Douglas	S	hard	31	2800	All structural uses, trim, woodwork, long ladder rails, doors. One of the chief commercial woods.	One of the strongest woods. Great tendency to check, split, shrink, swell. Needs primer to hold paint.

184

					Uses	Remarks
Fir, balsam	S	medium	25	1450	Framing, trim, and cabinetwork.	Needs filler for painting.
Gum, red	H	medium	34	1750	Int. finish, millwork, doors, veneer, furniture, trim.	Uniform texture, cross-grained. Beautiful natural figure. Stains perfectly.
Gum, black	H	medium	35	1750	Not widely used or marketed. About the same as above in use and qualities.	
Hemlock, eastern	S	medium	28	1750	Used extensively for building purposes. Inferior to pine.	Splinters easily, does not hold paint, is not decay resistant.
Hemlock, western	S	medium	29	2100	Framing, sheathing, subfloors, doors, sash, blinds, millwork.	Available in wide sizes. Uniform texture. Low resistance to decay.
Hickory, pecan	H	hard	45	3100	Wagon tongues, tool handles, skis, golf clubs, wheel spokes, etc.	Extremely hard, tough, strong, and elastic. Rubs to good finish.
Hickory, true	H	hard	51	3100	Same uses as above.	Somewhat tougher than pecan variety. Both are inclined to decay in wet.

COMMON NAME	WORK CLASS [a]	QUALITY [b]	WEIGHT [c]	BASIC STRESS [d]	GENERAL USES	OTHER QUALITIES
Larch (tamarack)	S	hard	36	2400	Stadium seats, decking, railroad ties, posts, interior construction, cabinetmaking, fencing.	Very durable wood. Fine, uniform grain. Finishes well with wax or varnish.
Locust, black	H	hard	48	n.d.	Fenceposts, turning stock, shipbuilding.	Hard and durable. Needs filler for painting.
Magnolia, cucumber	H	medium	33	n.d.	Interior finishing, cabinetmaking. Often substitute for poplar.	Light and soft. Takes a beautiful natural finish or paint.
Maple, hard (sugar maple)	H	hard	42	2400	Principal cabinet and furniture wood, flooring, stair treads, panels.	Fine natural luster. Very stable when properly kiln dried.
Maple, soft (silver)	H	hard	35	n.d.	Limited use. Trim, furniture, and paneling.	Soft and subject to insect larvae attack.
Oak, red	H	hard	44	2250	Principal flooring and furniture wood, all grades of interior finish, trim.	Extremely hard, stiff, and strong. Coarse grained and porous.

					Uses	Characteristics
Oak, white	H	hard	47	2250	More desirable than the red oak for fine furniture.	Same as above, but more decay resistant.
Pine, Idaho white (western)	S	easy	27	1450	Sash, doors, blinds, matches, patterns, knotty pine paneling, turnings.	Shrinks and swells with humidity. Grain is straight. Durable.
Pine, longleaf southern (Georgia pitch)	S	hard	41	2800	Principal construction material, scaffolds, siding, timbers, bridges, docks.	Highly resinous, checks and splits. Does not hold paint.
Pine, northern white (soft white)	S	easy	25	1450	Ideal pattern wood, sash, doors, blinds, matches, carving, paneling.	Fine texture and close grained. Little shrinking or swelling.
Pine, ponderosa	S	easy	28	1450	General house building, all parts, millwork, all white pine uses, paneling, etc.	Fine grain, excellent insulator, finishes any choice.
Pine, shortleaf (southern)	S	hard	36	2400	General utility, flooring, doors, planing mill, trim. More useful than longleaf.	Straight grained and moderately resinous. Takes paint well.

187

COMMON NAME	CLASS [a]	WORK QUALITY [b]	WEIGHT [c]	BASIC STRESS [d]	GENERAL USES	OTHER QUALITIES
Pine, sugar	S	easy	25	1450	"King of pines" for cabinet, carving, patterns, fancy woodwork, trim, blinds.	More durable, less shrink and twist than other pines.
Poplar, yellow	H	easy	28	1450	Very extensive interior use. Trim, moldings, sash, doors, cabinets, etc.	Durable, stains uniformly and takes paint smoothly.
Redwood	S	medium	28	2000	All weathered places. Interior trim, paneling, beamed ceilings, high grade millwork.	Boards are wide and clear. Very stable and smooth to paint.
Spruce, eastern	S	medium	28	1750	Better grades for patterns and musical instruments. Framing, boxes.	Very strong, not decay resistant, soft and satiny texture.
Spruce, Engelmann	S	easy	23	1200	Sporting goods, cabinetwork, built-in furniture, step ladders, aircraft.	Not resistant to decay. Takes fine finish and paints well.

188

Spruce, Sitka	S	medium	28	1750	Aircraft and trailer frame, ext. and int. finish, trim, mill-work products.	Large-size boards. Straight grain and free of warping.
Sycamore (plane tree)	H	medium	34	n.d.	Interior trim, fancy panels, veneers, doors, furniture.	Highly figured surface, takes a wax or natural finish.
Walnut, black	H	medium	38	n.d.	Very important wood for fine furniture, veneers, gun stocks, cabinetwork, interior trim.	Rich color and distinct figure.

189

TABLE 2

Board Measure of One Lineal Foot

WIDTH IN INCHES	THICKNESS IN INCHES									
	1	2	3	4	5	6	7	8	9	10
18	1.5	3.0	4.5	6.0	7.5	9.0	10.5	12.0	13.5	15.0
17	1.4	2.8	4.2	5.6	7.1	8.5	9.9	11.3	12.7	14.1
16	1.3	2.6	4.0	5.3	6.7	8.0	9.3	10.6	12.0	13.3
15	1.2	2.5	3.7	5.0	6.2	7.5	8.7	10.0	11.2	12.5
14	1.2	2.3	3.5	4.6	5.8	7.0	8.1	9.3	10.5	11.7
13	1.1	2.2	3.2	4.3	5.4	6.5	7.6	8.7	9.8	10.8
12	1.0	2.0	3.0	4.0	5.0	6.0	7.0	8.0	9.0	10.0
11	.9	1.8	2.3	3.7	4.6	5.5	6.4	7.3	8.3	9.2
10	.8	1.7	2.5	3.3	4.2	5.0	5.8	6.7	7.5	8.3
9	.8	1.5	2.2	3.0	3.8	4.5	5.3	6.0	6.8	—
8	.7	1.3	2.0	2.7	3.3	4.0	4.7	5.3	—	—
7	.6	1.2	1.7	2.3	2.9	3.5	4.1	—	—	—
6	.5	1.0	1.5	2.0	2.5	3.0	—	—	—	—
5	.4	.8	1.3	1.7	2.1	—	—	—	—	—
4	.3	.7	1.0	1.3	—	—	—	—	—	—
3	.3	.5	.8	—	—	—	—	—	—	—
2	.2	.3	—	—	—	—	—	—	—	—

NOTE: The above figures are approximations only. The fractions would have to be carried out to three decimal places to be accurate. The table is intended only as a rough computation for estimating.

EXAMPLE: Needing a piece of lumber 2 inches thick by 8 inches wide and 10 feet long, the workman would have to know the number of board feet required to estimate the cost. He need look down the left hand column of the table to the figure 8, the width of the board. Moving across on this line to the column under 2, the thickness, he finds the figure 1.3. Multiplying 1.3 by 10, the length, he finds that he needs 13 board feet of lumber.

TABLE 3

Decimal Equivalents of Wire, Letter, and Fractional-Size Drills

Drill Size No.	Decimal	Drill Size No.	Decimal	Drill Size No.	Decimal
80	.0135	29	.1360	21/64	.3281
79	.0145	28	.1405	Q	.3320
1/64	.0156	9/64	.1406	R	.3390
78	.0160	27	.1440	11/32	.3437
77	.0180	26	.1470	S	.3480
76	.0200	25	.1495	T	.3580
75	.0210	24	.1520	23/64	.3594
74	.0225	23	.1540	U	.3680
73	.0240	5/32	.1562	3/8	.3750
72	.0250	22	.1570	V	.3770
71	.0260	21	.1590	W	.3860
70	.0280	20	.1610	25/64	.3906
69	.0292	19	.1660	X	.3970
68	.0310	18	.1695	Y	.4040
1/32	.0312	11/64	.1719	13/32	.4062
67	.0320	17	.1730	Z	.4130
66	.0330	16	.1770	27/64	.4219
65	.0350	15	.1800	7/16	.4375
64	.0360	14	.1820	29/64	.4531
63	.0370	13	.1850	15/32	.4687
62	.0380	3/16	.1875	31/64	.4844
61	.0390	12	.1890	1/2	.5000
60	.0400	11	.1910	33/64	.5156
59	.0410	10	.1935	17/32	.5312
58	.0420	9	.1960	35/64	.5469
57	.0430	8	.1990	9/16	.5625
56	.0465	7	.2010	37/64	.5781
3/64	.0469	13/64	.2031	19/32	.5937
55	.0520	6	.2040	39/64	.6094
54	.0550	5	.2055	5/8	.6250
53	.0595	4	.2090	41/64	.6406
1/16	.0625	3	.2130	21/32	.6562
52	.0635	7/32	.2187	43/64	.6719
51	.0670	2	.2210	11/16	.6875
50	.0700	1	.2280	45/64	.7031
49	.0730	A	.2340	23/32	.7187
48	.0760	15/64	.2344	47/64	.7344
5/64	.0781	B	.2380	3/4	.7500
47	.0785	C	.2420	49/64	.7656
46	.0810	D	.2460	25/32	.7812
45	.0820	E 1/4	.2500	51/64	.7969
44	.0860	F	.2570	13/16	.8125
43	.0890	G	.2610	53/64	.8281
42	.0935	17/64	.2656	27/32	.8437
3/32	.0937	H	.2660	55/64	.8594
41	.0960	I	.2720	7/8	.8750
40	.0980	J	.2770	57/64	.8906
39	.0995	K	.2810	29/32	.9062
38	.1015	9/32	.2812	59/64	.9219
37	.1040	L	.2900	15/16	.9375
36	.1065	M	.2950	61/64	.9531
7/64	.1094	19/64	.2969	31/32	.9687
35	.1100	N	.3020	63/64	.9844
34	.1110	5/16	.3125	1	1.0000
33	.1130	O	.3160		
32	.1160	P	.3230		
31	.1200				
1/8	.1250				
30	.1285				

TABLE 4

Screw Chart—Drill and Bit Sizes

SIZE OF SCREW	BIT OR DRILL SIZES					AUGER BIT FOR COUNTER-SINK (By 16ths)
	SHANK HOLES		PILOT HOLES			
			Hard Wood		Soft Wood	
	Drill number or letter	Drill Size nearest fraction	Drill number or letter	Drill size nearest fraction	Drill number or letter	Drill size nearest fraction	
0	52	$\frac{1}{16}''$	70	$\frac{1}{32}''$	75	$\frac{1}{64}''$	—
1	47	$\frac{5}{64}''$	66	$\frac{1}{32}''$	71	$\frac{1}{32}''$	—
2	42	$\frac{3}{32}''$	56	$\frac{3}{64}''$	65	$\frac{1}{32}''$	3
3	37	$\frac{7}{64}''$	54	$\frac{1}{16}''$	58	$\frac{3}{64}''$	4
4	32	$\frac{7}{64}''$	52	$\frac{1}{16}''$	55	$\frac{3}{64}''$	4
5	30	$\frac{1}{8}''$	49	$\frac{5}{64}''$	53	$\frac{1}{16}''$	4
6	27	$\frac{9}{64}''$	47	$\frac{5}{64}''$	52	$\frac{1}{16}''$	5
7	22	$\frac{5}{32}''$	44	$\frac{3}{32}''$	51	$\frac{1}{16}''$	5
8	18	$\frac{11}{64}''$	40	$\frac{3}{32}''$	48	$\frac{5}{64}''$	6
9	14	$\frac{3}{16}''$	37	$\frac{7}{64}''$	45	$\frac{5}{64}''$	6
10	10	$\frac{3}{16}''$	33	$\frac{7}{64}''$	43	$\frac{3}{32}''$	6
11	4	$\frac{13}{64}''$	31	$\frac{1}{8}''$	40	$\frac{3}{32}''$	7
12	2	$\frac{7}{32}''$	30	$\frac{1}{8}''$	38	$\frac{7}{64}''$	7
14	D	$\frac{1}{4}''$	25	$\frac{9}{64}''$	32	$\frac{7}{64}''$	8
16	I	$\frac{17}{64}''$	18	$\frac{5}{32}''$	29	$\frac{9}{64}''$	9
18	N	$\frac{19}{64}''$	13	$\frac{3}{16}''$	26	$\frac{9}{64}''$	10
20	P	$\frac{21}{64}''$	4	$\frac{13}{64}''$	19	$\frac{11}{64}''$	11
24	V	$\frac{3}{8}''$	1	$\frac{7}{32}''$	15	$\frac{3}{16}''$	12

Black & Decker Manufacturing Company

TABLE 5

Abrasive Chart for Use with Portable Sanders

WOODS	Roughing	Finishing	Fine Finishing
OAK	2½ to 1½A	½ to 1/0G	2/0 to 4/0G
MAPLE	2½ to 1A	½ to 1/0G	2/0 to 4/0G
BIRCH	2½ to 1A	½ to 1/0G	2/0 to 4/0G
WALNUT	2½ to 1½A	½ to 1/0G	2/0 to 4/0G
MAHOGANY	2½ to 1½A	½ to 1/0G	2/0 to 3/0G
GUM	2½ to 1½A	½ to 1/0G	2/0 to 3/0G
CURLY MAPLE	2½ to 1½A	½ to 1/0G	2/0 to 4/0G
CYPRESS	2½ to 1½A	½ to 1/0A	2/0G
INDOAKO	1½A	½ to 1/0G	2/0 to 4/0G
FIR	1½ to 1A	½ to 1/0G	2/0G
WHITE PINE	1½ to 1G	1/0G	2/0G
YELLOW PINE	2 to 1½SA	½G	1/0G
WILLOW	2A	½ to 1/0G	2/0G
School Desks	3SA	1½ to ½A	1/0 to 2/0G
Slate Blackboards	80-100T	120 to 150T	
Removing Paint and Varnish	3½ to 2½SA Spaced Grain	A solution of three parts kerosene and one part light lubricating oil wiped lightly over varnished surface before sanding will increase belt service.	

Symbols: G—Garnet for soft wood. A—Artificial for hard wood. M—Aluminum Oxide for ferrous metals. SA—Spaced for paint or varnish. T—Silicon Carbide for stone, marble, glass, aluminum and non-ferrous metals.

TABLE 6

Abrasive Recommendations for Finishing Sanders

KIND OF MATERIAL	MATERIAL REMOVAL		MATERIAL REMOVAL WITH FAIR FINISH		FINE FINISH		RUBBING (Use No. 1300Y Special Rubbing Pad)
	GRIT	SIZE OF GRIT	GRIT	OF GRIT SIZE	GRIT	OF GRIT SIZE	
Soft Wood Soft Wallboard	Cabinet Paper (Garnet)	2-1	Cabinet Paper (Garnet)	1/2-2/0	Finishing Paper (Garnet)	3/0-5/0	Abrasives with Lubricants 1. Rouge with water 2. Silica Smoke with water 3. Any branded silicon carbide abrasives with water
Plastics	Cabinet Paper (Aluminum Oxide)	60-100	Wet Paper "C" Weight (Silicon Carbide)	120-220	Wet Paper "A" Weight (Silicon Carbide)	240-600	Lubricants Containing Abrasives 1. "Noxon" 2. "Porter's Friend" 3. Any standard metal polish
Hard Wood Hard Compositions Wallboards, Etc.	Cabinet Paper (Aluminum Oxide)	36-50	Cabinet Paper (Aluminum Oxide)	60-100	Finishing Paper (Aluminum Oxide)	120-180	
Soft Metals	Metal Working Cloth (Aluminum Oxide)	36-60	Cabinet Paper (Aluminum Oxide)	80-120	Wet Paper (Silicon Carbide)	150-320	Abrasives with Lubricants 1. Diamond dust with kerosene 2. Diamontine with kerosene 3. Free aluminum oxide with machine oil or water-soluble oil 4. Powdered alumina with kerosene 5. Rouge with kerosene or machine oil 6. Silica Smoke with machine oil
Hard Metals	Metal Working Cloth (Aluminum Oxide)	40-60	Metal Working Cloth (Aluminum Oxide)	80-120	Metal Working Cloth in Oil (Aluminum Oxide)	150-320 or crocus	
Hard Brittle Minerals and Compositions	Cabinet Paper (Aluminum Oxide)	50-80	Finishing Paper (Aluminum Oxide)	100-180	Wet Paper "A" Weight (Silicon Carbide)	220-320	Abrasives with Lubricants 1. Pumice powder with linseed oil soap solution, palm oil or crude oil. Rotten stone with oil
Hard Tough Minerals and Compositions	Metal Working Cloth (Aluminum Oxide)		Metal Working Cloth (Aluminum Oxide)	80-120	Finishing Paper (Aluminum Oxide)	150-320	Lubricants Containing Abrasives
Paints and Varnishes	Cabinet Paper (Open-coat Garnet)	2 1/2-1 1/2			Wet Paper "A" Weight (Silicon Carbide)	240-400	Abrasives Rubbing compounds with cheesecloth pad 2. Simonize with cheesecloth or lambswool pad

TABLE 7

Trade Names of Abrasive Materials

MANU-FACTURER	TYPE OF ABRASIVE AND TRADE NAMES FOR PAPERS & CLOTHS				TRADE NAMES FOR COATING		
	Aluminum Oxide Cabinet or Finishing Paper	Garnet Cabinet or Finishing Paper	Aluminum Oxide Metal Working Cloth	Silicon Carbide Paper	Water-proof Paper	Electro-Coated	Open Coat
Armour	Garalun	H. T. Garnet	Alundum	Crystolon	Rub-wet	Electro-Coated	Amour-ite
Behr Manning	Adalox	Garnet	Metalite	Durite	Speed-wet	Light-ning	Open Kote
Carbor-undum	Cabinet or Finishing Paper-Alo	Cabinet or Finishing Paper-Garnet	Metal Cloth	Abrasive Cloth or Paper	Water-proof	Electro-Coated	Open
Minnesota Mining & Manu-facturing	Produc-tion	Garnet	Three-M-Ite	Tri-M-Ite	Wet or Dry	Elek-Tro-Cut	Cutrite

NOTE: If closed coat abrasives are desired, specify "closed coat" when ordering

TABLE 8

Comparative Grading Chart for Abrasives

GRAIN SIZE (*mesh*)	CORUNDUM AND EMERY CLOTH	FLINT PAPER	GARNET, SILICON CARBIDE, ALUMINUM OXIDE
320 (very fine)			10/0
240 " "		5/0	7/0
220 " "		4/0	6/0
200 (fine)		3/0	
180 "	3/0		5/0
150 "	2/0		4/0
136 "		2/0	
120 "			3/0
110 "	0	0	
100 "			2/0
90 (medium)	1/2	1/2	
80 "	1		0
70 "	1½	1	
60 "			1/2
56 "	2		
50 "		1½	1
40 (coarse)	2½	2	1½
36 "			2
30 "	3	3	2½
24 (very coarse)			3
20 " "			3½
16 " "			4

TABLE 9

Recommended Extension Cord Sizes for Use with Portable Electric Tools

Nameplate Amperes	CORD LENGTH IN FEET																			
	25	50	75	100	125	150	175	200	225	250	275	300	325	350	375	400	425	450	475	500
1	16	16	16	16	16	16	16	16	16	16	16	16	16	16	16	16	16	16	16	14
2	16	16	16	16	16	16	16	16	16	14	14	14	14	14	14	12	12	12	12	12
3	16	16	16	16	16	16	14	14	14	12	12	12	12	12	12	12	10	10	10	10
4	16	16	16	16	14	14	14	12	12	12	12	10	10	10	10	10	10	10	10	10
5	14	14	14	14	14	14	12	12	12	12	10	10	10	10	8	8	8	8	8	8
6	14	14	14	14	12	12	12	10	10	10	10	8	8	8	8	8	8	8	8	8
7	14	14	14	14	12	12	12	10	10	10	8	8	8	8	8	8	8	8	8	
8	14	14	14	12	12	12	10	10	10	8	8	8	8	8	8	8	8	8	8	
9	14	14	14	12	12	10	10	10	10	8	8	8	8	8	8	8	8			
10	14	14	12	12	10	10	10	10	8	8	8	8	8	8	8					
11	12	12	12	10	10	10	10	8	8	8	8	8	8							
12	12	12	12	10	10	10	8	8	8	8	8	8								
13	12	12	12	10	10	10	8	8	8	8	8									
14	10	10	10	10	10	10	8	8	8	8	8									
15	10	10	10	10	10	8	8	8	8	8										
16	10	10	10	10	10	8	8	8	8	8										
17	10	10	10	10	10	8	8	8	8											
18	8	8	8	8	8	8	8	8	8											
19	8	8	8	8	8	8	8	8												
20	8	8	8	8	8	8	8	8												

NOTE: Wire sizes shown are A.W.G. (American Wire Gauge).

TABLE 10

Handy Shop Formulas

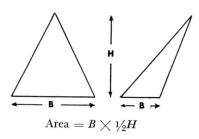

Area $= B \times \frac{1}{2}H$

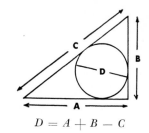

$D = A + B - C$

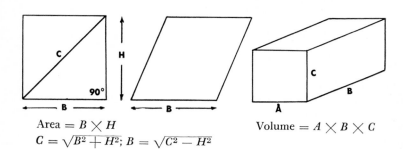

Area $= B \times H$
$C = \sqrt{B^2 + H^2}; B = \sqrt{C^2 - H^2}$

Volume $= A \times B \times C$

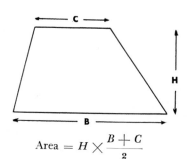

Area $= H \times \dfrac{B + C}{2}$

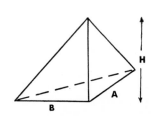

Volume $= \dfrac{(\frac{1}{2}B \times A) \times H}{3}$

TABLE 10 (*cont.*)

Handy Shop Formulas

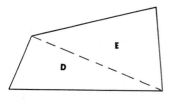

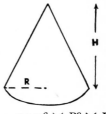

Area = Area *D* + Area *E*   Volume = $\dfrac{3.1416 \times R^2 \times H}{3}$

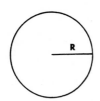

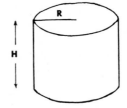

Area = $R^2 \times 3.1416$ Volume = $3.1416 \times R^2 \times H$

Area = Circumference $\times \dfrac{R}{2}$

Circumference = $2R \times 3.1416$

TABLE 11

Common Weights and Measures

MEASURES OF LENGTH

Inches	Feet	Yards	Rods	Furlongs	Mile
12	1				
36	3	1			
198	16½	5½	1		
7920	660	220	40	1	
63,360	5280	1760	320	8	1

1 nautical mile (knot) equals 6,080.26 feet.

MEASURES OF SURFACE

Sq. Inch	Sq. Feet	Sq. Yard	Sq. Rods	Acre
144	1			
1296	9	1		
39,204	272¼	30¼	1	
1,568,160	10,890	1210	40	
6,272,640	43,560	4840	160	1

640 acres equal 1 square mile.

MEASURES OF VOLUME

Cubic Inches	Cubic Feet	Cubic Yards
1728	1	
46,656	27	1

One cord equals 4 feet x 4 feet x 8 feet equals 128 cu. ft.

MEASURES OF WEIGHT

Grains	Drachms	Ounces	Pounds	Tons
437.5	16	1		
7000	256	16	1	
		32,000	2000	1

1 gross or long ton equals 2,240 pounds.

TABLE 11 (*cont.*)

Common Weights and Measures

MEASURES OF ARCS OF THE CIRCLE

Minutes	Degrees	Quadrants	Circle
60	1		
5400	90	1	
21,600	360	4	1

MEASURES OF LIQUID

Gills	Pints	Quarts	Gallons	Barrels	Hogsheads
4	1				
8	2	1			
32	8	4	1		
1008	252	126	31½	1	
2016	504	252	63	2	1

NOTE: The U. S. gallon contains 231 cubic inches and, at maximum density, one gallon of water weighs 8.345 pounds.

METRIC MEASURES OF LENGTH

1 meter equals 39.37 inches or 3.28 feet or 1.09 yards
.305 meter equals 1 foot
25.40 millimeters (mm) equals 1 inch
1 kilometer equals 1,093.61 yards or .621 miles.

INDEX

INDEX